Contents

1. Introduction

1.1. The intention of 20th century man not only to live, but to live well, and the brilliant multi-faceted technology which he has to hand in pursuing this objective, has brought the human race up sharply against the margins - an expanding and unthinking use of place and resources has been starkly shown to be up against the limits of a finite world. This is an increasing new dimension in our perception of the need for expansion and development.

1.2. It is not simply the result of advancing technology. Since 1900 the world population has increased by about 3bn. By 2000 there will be over 1bn more. Not only the numbers but the age structure will be radically different from the mid-century. Those over 60 represented 20% in 1981, as opposed to 7.5% in 1901. The number of vehicles in the UK has risen from 8,000 in 1903 to over 19M in 1987. Taken together all the factors make for a revolution in the way we approach proposals for new developments.

1.3. The Institution of Civil Engineers has attempted to keep pace with the changing spectrum of ideas. In 1984 the ICE published a report on infrastructure, with the intention of identifying priorities in the use of those resources. In 1988 there was a report on 'Urban regeneration'. Last year saw the report on 'Congestion' and this year's report deals with the whole environment. Taken together they represent a body of work with a consistent theme.

1.4. The impetus for this work arises because the civil engineer is uniquely placed to advise on the infrastructure of society, and its impact on the environment. Civil engineers plan, construct, manage and maintain the greater part of the infrastructure and as a result there is no professional better placed to identify the problems, and to recommend and carry into effect the solutions. Our predecessors, who laid the foundations in terms of drainage, clean water and transport, were able to pursue those developments in the public interest only constrained in the main by topography, powerful landowners and city fathers. They were able to direct the great sources of power in nature for the use and convenience of man without much regard for environmental questions. Brunel could drive his black britzska* across the country to set out the line for the Great Western Railway without a great deal of heed to other than physical limitations. This is no longer possible.

1.5. Not the least reason for this in the UK is population change. Although conditions vary from country to country, pollution and pressures on the environment are bound to be linked in a general way with the density of population. The density of population in the UK ($660/mile^2$) is twice that of France ($270/mile^2$) and ten times that of the United States ($70/mile^2$). There are a few developed countries with even higher densities of population, notably Japan ($850/mile^2$) and the Netherlands ($1100/mile^2$), and environmental pressures (and land prices) in those countries have also risen sharply. The impact of present trends of population in the UK is even more significant when component national figures are considered separately. Scotland with over a third of the land area of the UK, has had a declining population for many years and projections assume this will continue. On the other hand England, with $940/mile^2$ at present, is projected as showing the greatest

---

* An open horse drawn carriage

increase in population. The Government Actuary's projections, based on experience in recent years and a number of assumptions regarding future trends, suggested that by the year 2000 there would be another 2M people in the UK, of which 1.4M would be in the South East.

1.6. These and other pressures have meant that an extra dimension, the environment, has to be taken into account, not least because public anxiety on that score has reached a point where the environment has become a political imperative. It is not possible to consider infrastructure, or development proposals, in any way apart from environmental impact. The civil engineer has long recognised his responsibility but now the terms on which such issues are dealt with must be more explicit. What should they be?

1.7. The civil engineer provides a service for public or private clients, who commission and pay for the work. Measures necessary to safeguard the environment must involve extra cost. There may occasionally be amongst the engineers' clients those so wedded to cost benefit as to instruct the engineer to disregard environmental safeguards in the well justified interests of competition. If the civil engineer refuses to do so, the commission may be taken elsewhere. If he accepts the instructions, he is assenting to a degradation of the environment which is repugnant to his professional ethic and status.

1.8. The predicament arises from the confrontation between the pressure for lowest practicable costs, and the need to ensure that these are not low at the cost of a degraded environment. If the importance of the latter is held in common by all parties, the difficulty does not arise. This is not however the case. Cost cutting is an essential part of competition. Only if society's view of the importance of the environment is jointly held by all parties can the calculation of cost be on a common base. Society's view of the matter can only be made effective if there are sanctions to uphold the need for environmental care. This view, and the sanctions to enforce it are unlikely to be effective unless they are embedded in legislation. Proper competition can only be ensured if legislation makes this possible. This report sets out the case for statutory provision to put beyond doubt the need for all new works to include an environmental assessment, and seeks to establish in respect of the main areas of civil engineering what those factors should be, and how they should be measured and enforced.

1.9. The scope of legislation must not be confined to the UK alone. If UK industry is to compete in Europe, it must be on the basis that Common Market competitors accept the same need to safeguard the environment. Unless this is so UK acceptance of responsibility would simply provide others with a competitive advantage. This means an EC Directive and recommendations on this score are contained in this report.

1.10. This must also be true of competition outside the Community since pollution spans one or more national boundaries, and arises where EC legislation has no place. Without, however, pressures to enforce respect for the environment from projects and developments coming from Eastern Europe, or the Third World, EC industry will suffer competitive disadvantage. There is a need for fiscal measures in the EC which neutralise this imbalance and the absence of such measures is a major defect in current EC environmental legislation.

1.11. The purpose of this report is to survey the impact of pollution on the environment, and to draw attention to the short and long term implications. It attempts to give recognition to the novel element in the present situation, which is that in the conflict between development and environmental protection the point of compromise has shifted in favour of the latter. The objective is to identify the new balance between these tensions, and point the way to resolving the difficulties that arise. It seeks to establish, where practicable, an optimal level of pollution consistent with sustainable development, in which damage is contained and the resilience of the environment is restored and maintained. In this, the role of the civil engineer is crucial.

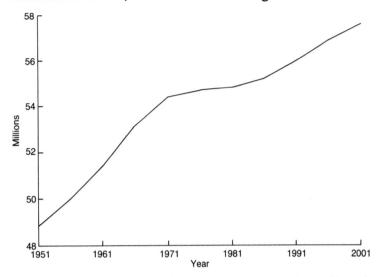

Figure 1.1. Projected population growth in Britain based on mid-1987 estimates. Source: Office of Population, Censuses and Surveys.*

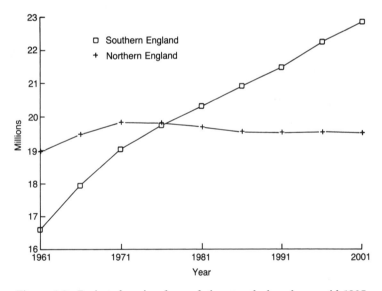

Figure 1.2. Projected regional population trends based on mid-1985 estimates. Source: Office of Population, Censuses and Surveys.*

*Southern England: East Midlands, East Anglia, South East (less Greater London), South West
Northern England: North, Yorkshire & Humberside, West Midlands, Northwest

2.   Summary and recommendations

Environmental pollution

2.1.   The Third World is in the middle of a surge in the level of population, with latest UN projections suggesting that global levels might reach 15bn by the end of the next century. This represents a key challenge of pollution to the environment which may not have the capacity to sustain such population growth.

2.2.   Opinions differ on the more complex global problems. Much of the scientific evidence for the 'greenhouse effect' is still uncertain, and the results of studies into the effects of natural climatic changes and temperature variations on the oceans and carbon cycle will not be established for some years. Long term research should be started immediately to develop a proper scientific base against which the problems can be assessed with acceptable accuracy. Government intervention is crucial since pollution of the environment is a classic example of market failure, and action by individuals or groups smaller than governments is likely to be ineffective.

Government intervention

2.3.   Government's role is inescapable for a further reason. It alone can impose taxation which represents a powerful tool to deal with environmental pollution, and one which is more efficient than administrative regulation. Taxes should penalise polluters for the external costs of their activities, in this way ensuring that they do not treat the environment as 'free'.

2.4.   Unilateral action to protect the environment increases costs and affects competitiveness. International agreement on a new regulatory framework is required before implementation. Some loss of economic sovereignty will have to be accepted in tackling pollution.

Environmental Impact Assessment

2.5.   The requirement for Environmental Impact Assessments should be made more effective. The EC Directive on Environmental Impact Assessment provides the procedure but it lacks statutory enforcement. Environmental Impact Assessment should be put on statutory basis, be required for all new developments, with cost/benefit analysis applied to the maximum extent.

Environmental Protection Agency

2.6.   The creation of an independent national regulatory body, an Environmental Protection Agency, is required to make effective the enforcement of policy, particularly as regards development by Government. An agency would enable international agreements to be brought more effectively into domestic policy.

Education

2.7.   Restraint in demand for energy and transport will not be achievable without a major campaign to inform the public of the lifestyle changes that will be necessary. Business managers and the public should be induced by fiscal measures to develop a positive attitude towards environmental safeguards.

Energy

2.8.   The possibility of world temperatures increasing due to the greenhouse effect is not proven, but after the Bergen Conference in May, the Government acknowledged the existence of global warming and announced support in principle for the control of carbon dioxide emissions. The finite nature of fossil fuels means that policy should be directed towards securing indefinite energy supplies, and establishing alternative options should it become necessary to limit carbon dioxide emissions in the future.

(a) The uptake of financially justified energy conservation measures by commercial and domestic sectors has been slow. Building regulations on the construction of new housing and offices should specify higher levels of energy conservation. Commercial organisations should be encouraged to appoint managers with responsibility for energy consumption. Schemes to give housing an energy rating and to encourage insulation should be supported.

(b) The development and use of combined heat and power schemes should be encouraged and capital restrictions placed on local authority expenditure on energy conservation should be eased.

(c) The UK has exceptional access to wind, wave and tidal energy sources and in these areas the Government should foster an international lead in research and development.

(d) Nuclear power has been proven as a relatively viable and safe power source, but it is distrusted by the public. Public confidence in the monitoring of safety needs to be restored. Further research is needed on the disposal of nuclear waste.

(e) Long term energy supply requires the establishment of a European fast breeder reactor programme, and greater financial commitment for international programmes on fusion research is required.

(f) Direct measures to reduce the consumption of fossil fuels should be introduced including a tax on carbon based fuel sources. The imposition of VAT on domestic fuel bills could promote energy conservation in the home.

2.9. Evidence of the damage caused by acid rain arising from the use of fossil fuels is conclusive. Reductions in the emission of sulphur oxides from power stations and oxides of nitrogen from power stations and motor vehicles must be achieved.

Transport

2.10. There is an urgent need for a coherent framework of national objectives for atmospheric emissions against which the development of transport infrastructure and land use planning can be assessed. Within the transport sector, road vehicles are the dominant source of emissions of carbon dioxide, hydrocarbons and nitrogen oxides. Government transport policy should encourage energy conservation through restricting the use of vehicles, by the introduction of financial measures:

(a) road pricing in cities
(b) increasing the price of petrol
(c) replacement of the annual car licence tax with an additional tax on petrol
(d) a tax system favouring cars with low emissions
(e) a tax imposed on HGVs reflecting the damage they impose on the environment.

2.11. Environmental Impact Assessment should be expanded on a comprehensive basis to apply to all new projects, and include local environmental disbenefits of noise, vibration and visual intrusion. Encouragement for pedestrians and cyclists by greater awareness of their needs in planning decisions is required.

(a) A reduction in the speed limit should be considered to reduce energy consumption, noise and accidents.

(b) Greater investment is required in public transport which is up to ten times more energy efficient than the private motor car.

2.12. Rail transport policy objectives should include

(a) encouragement for the transfer of passengers and freight from road to rail

(b)   the adoption of measures to mitigate noise from railways, including changes at the wheel/rail interface, the use of barriers and the adoption of noise level regulations

(c)   the implementation of measures outlined in the Central London Rail Study

(d)   investment by the Government, justified on similar criteria to investment in new or improved roads

(e)   the promotion of light rail systems in British cities.

2.13. The demand for air transport by the turn of the century will outstrip facilities. A realistic assessment of need and a coherent strategic plan for the UK is required now in order to safeguard the future prosperity of the United Kingdom's national and international status as a carrier.

Water and public health

2.14. Arrangements for the protection of the water supply are vulnerable to accidents, or deliberate acts of non-compliance, or where problems cross one or more boundaries of existing authorities. Response to these problems needs coordination backed by authority. Since the water cycle cannot be divorced from wider environmental issues, the principle of river basin management should be expanded and brought within the environmental framework for the UK as a whole, and made a responsibility of an Environmental Protection Agency.

(a)   Safe and adequate water quality can only be secured by a combination of investment, technology, management, planning and vigilance.

(b)   Effective management of the water cycle requires comprehensive regulation by an independent agency with adequate resources, defined accountability and the ability to coordinate other regulatory activity in the wider environment.

(c)   Innovative measures and stringent penalties are necessary for protecting groundwater from pollution.

(d)   The Government has undertaken an international commitment regarding the future disposal of sewage at sea and the marine dumping of sewage sludge. Transfer to the land environment of these products will introduce additional costs and demand more exacting disposal technologies.

(e)   In the sewage system, industrial wastes produce sewage sludges containing heavy metals and other pollutants which can create difficulties at the treatment stage. The practicability of treating industrial effluents and the effect on volume of diluting flow on sewage treatment processes should be examined as a matter of urgency.

Waste

2.15. Much waste is of value and the Government should provide a legal framework and financial incentives to ensure its maximum use. The key to recycling is the establishment of a stable market for the end product. Centralised research funded by an industrial levy is required.

(a)   New uses for waste need to be studied to encourage recycling and to reduce the problem of disposal.

(b)   Old landfill sites and contaminated land should be regulated more effectively by more stringent measures.

(c)   More schemes for methane generation, its collection on a commercial scale and use in generating electricity are required.

(d)   Further research into the development of waste derived fuels should be pursued.

(e)   Greater investment in research into the production of degradable plastics is required.

(f)   The problem of litter is growing and attention should be paid to the underfunding of municipal waste collection and street cleansing.

(g) Taxes on the toxic wastes of industry should be introduced on the principle that the 'polluter pays'.

(h) Financial incentives are required to encourage manufacturers to introduce new processes and plants to recycle waste products.

Coastal problems

2.16. The Government should develop a national plan on coastal defence which will include clear regional strategic plans for local authorities. Funds are required to maintain the present level of protection.

(a) The total environmental effect of a possible sea level rise should be assessed in studies based on cost benefit analysis.

(b) A combination of 'hard' (sea walls and revetments) and 'soft' (dunes and beaches) defences will be required.

(c) The scale and urgency of the problems facing coastal engineering demands much greater research, which should be on a broader base and coordinated. Research into data on the wave climate in the coastal area, unless organised nationally, is unlikely to be productive.

(d) In vulnerable coastal areas development will have to be subject to additional controls.

(e) The environmental effects of new proposals for offshore extraction should be examined closely within a wider framework.

Urban planning

2.17. Planning controls and regulations on developers should be strengthened by the Government to include environmental concerns.

(a) There is a need for development plans which give full coverage of the land area to provide sound bases for development control.

(b) It should be a statutory requirement that local authorities obtain an environmental assessment for defined developments at the outline planning stage.

(c) Specific design requirements should be incorporated in planning briefs to promote a satisfactory level of environmental quality.

(d) Planning principles should include the need to minimise the use of vehicles, and the need to integrate road, rail, pedestrian and cycle routes.

(e) The needs and control of the extractive industries require comprehensive oversight of source and utilisation to minimise environmental damage. Research into recycling of construction materials needs encouragement to reduce extraction of primary materials. Planning permission should include consideration of the site after extraction or mining has been completed.

3.   Energy

Introduction

Table 3.1. World energy production 1986

	1bn tonnes oil equivalent (toe)	%
Solid	2.1	31
Liquid	3.0	43
Gas	1.5	21
Electricity	0.3	4
Total	6.9	

Electricity comprises hydro and nuclear generated electricity.
Source: UNEP Environmental Data Report 1989/90.

Patterns of energy use
Production

Table 3.2. The Energy Crisis?

	Years supply
Bituminous and anthracitic coals	193
Sub-bituminous coals / lignite	370
Crude oil and natural gas liquids	33
Natural gas	57

Based on proven reserves used at current rates of consumption.
Source: UNEP Environmental Data Report 1989/90.

Global consumption

3.1.   This chapter reviews the main adverse impacts the use of energy is said to be having on the environment, considers possible future developments, and discusses ways of resolving some of the problems.

3.2.   The principal adverse effects can be summarised as follows

(a)   the greenhouse effect
(b)   acid rain and smog
(c)   radiation from the nuclear fuel cycle
(d)   disposal of solid waste.

3.3.   In recent years major concern about energy focused on the finite nature of resources - the so called energy crisis. Now at the beginning of the 1990s, the energy crisis seems to have given way to the apparent threat from the greenhouse effect, rising world sea levels, and acid rain. It should be made clear that the possibility of a greenhouse effect has been acknowledged for several decades. And although scientific circles await conclusive evidence of its effect, concern has crossed national boundaries in a way that was not the case over the energy crisis.

3.4.   Table 3.1 lists the present world energy production. Dependence on fossil fuel sources is almost total, providing 96% of all energy. Policies to prevent the onset of the greenhouse effect would place a constraint on the use of fossil fuels. While the greenhouse effect is yet to be universally accepted, there is no dispute that the resources of fossil fuels are finite. Table 3.2 shows how long proven reserves of fossil fuels will last at current rates of depletion, although the reality of the situation is a little more subtle. As the price of a fuel increases, sources that were previously uneconomic become viable. For example, in the North Sea there are marginal oilfields which could be exploited were the price of oil sufficiently high. Increased price also acts as an incentive to discover new resources. Fossil fuel resources have been consistently underestimated. Against this is the prospect that world demand for energy will increase substantially as the industrialisation of South America, Africa and Asia gathers pace.

3.5.   The ultimate constraint on an energy resource is the net energy gain. To utilise energy sources requires an initial input of energy. In the case of coal, explosives are used to fracture the rock, large amounts of spoil must be excavated and disposed of, and the coal must finally be extracted and transported to the customer.

3.6.   Because the majority of the world's population as yet consumes little energy, there is a vast potential for increased consumption. The top fifth of the world's population consumes two-thirds of the energy. If the entire world had the same per capita energy consumption as the norm for the United States, total energy consumption would increase by a factor of 5 and the world would exhaust its proven reserves of oil in six years, and of coal in about 60 years.

3.7.   Comparison of the patterns of consumption between different countries indicates how the demand for energy changes with increasing living standards and shows where conservation measures are likely to have the greatest overall effect. For this, it is important to identify the factors which underlie energy consumption. Comparison of the

Table 3.3. Per capita consumption of energy, 1987

	Tonnes of oil equivalent (toe)					
	FRG	USA	Sweden	UK	Switzerland	Japan
Total	**3.3**	**3.3**	**4.1**	**2.6**	**2.9**	**2.1**
Industry	1.1	1.0	1.5	0.8	0.6	1.0
Transport	0.8	1.2	0.9	0.7	0.8	0.5
Commerce	0.4	0.4	0.5	0.2	0.5	0.2
Residential	0.8	0.6	1.0	0.7	0.9	0.3

Source: OECD Energy Balances.

Table 3.4. Percentage of passenger kilometres travelled by rail

	% distance travelled by rail	Per capita energy consumption (toe)
USA	0.4	1.2
Sweden	6.4	0.9
FRG	6.6	0.8
UK	7.1	0.7
Switzerland	12.6	0.8
Japan	40.1	0.5

Source: Derived from OECD energy balances.

figures for a selection of western economies (Table 3.3) suggests that there is little relation between GDP and total energy consumption. There is a correlation between GDP and personal travel. It is notable that countries with a well developed and patronised public transport system use significantly less energy (Table 3.4).

3.8. Whereas in western type economies energy consumption is static and in some cases in decline, for the world as a whole, prospects for increased energy use is considerable.

UK consumption

3.9. Total energy consumption in the UK as indicated in Table 3.5 was growing at a rate of around 2% per annum during the 1960s but has progressively tailed off so that the energy consumption was effectively static during the 1980s. The table shows how petroleum and gas have supplanted coal as the UK's most important source of energy.

3.10. Energy consumption by individual sectors has changed significantly (Table 3.6). The decline in the industrial use of energy has been entirely taken up by an increase in the transport and domestic sectors. Over half of the increase in the transport sector is a result of the increased use of road transport. The distance travelled by vehicles in the UK increased by 42% over this period. Growth in traffic is forecast to continue and with it will go an increased consumption of energy that is likely to overwhelm any reductions in other sectors.

Table 3.5. Energy consumption for UK - inland consumption of primary fuels

	M tonnes coal equivalent			
	1958	1968	1978	1988
Coal	201.8	167.3	119.9	112.0
Petroleum	49.1	129.1	39.3	116.1
Natural gas	0.1	4.8	65.1	81.5
Nuclear electricity	0.1	10.2	13.4	22.9
Hydro	1.5	1.9	2.2	2.4
Electricity imports	-	-	-	5.2
Total	**252.6**	**313.6**	**339.9**	**334.9**

Source: Digest of UK Energy Statistics.

Table 3.6. UK consumption of energy by sector

1978=100	1978	1980	1982	1984	1986	1988
Industry	100	85	77	73	72	75
Transport	100	102	101	109	118	131
Domestic	100	102	101	97	114	108
Other	100	97	96	98	100	102
Total	**100**	**95**	**91**	**91**	**97**	**100**

Source: Digest of UK Energy Statistics.

Energy and the future

3.11. Western economies have been reducing their use of energy. Their increases in GDP are associated with expansion of the commercial sector and of light industry which are low users of energy. Increase in the use of road transport is likely to be the most significant cause of increased energy consumption.

3.12. Second and Third World countries are well below the standards of living and energy consumption of the West. Because these countries tend to be centred around tropical zones the demand for heating may not materialise, but there is considerable potential need for energy for cooling and a massive potential for increase in energy demand in the transportation and industrial sectors.

Carbon dioxide and the greenhouse effect

Table 3.7. Contributions to man-made global warming

Carbon dioxide		55%
Power stations	11%	
Other energy sources	29%	
Deforestation	15%	
Methane		20%
CFCs		15%
Nitrous oxide		5%
Tropospheric ozone		5%

Source: Tolland & Donaldson UKAEA.

Table 3.8. Carbon dioxide emissions - ground-based sources 1986

Power stations	37%
Domestic	20%
Industry	19%
Transport	18%
Services	4%
Refineries	3%

Source: EER emissions model.

More efficient production

Table 3.9. Fuel into heat

	Efficiency
Conventional boiler	70-80%
Condensing boiler	90%

Table 3.10. Efficiencies of energy conversion

Domestic boiler	80%	Heat
Power station	35%	Electricity
Diesel engine	30%	Motion
Petrol engine	20%	Motion
Light bulb	6%	Light
Using electricity		
Electric fire	100%	Heat
Electric motor	90%	Motion

Improving thermal efficiency
Motion

3.13. This section considers what options there are available to reduce the emission of carbon dioxide, taking into account that carbon dioxide is only one of a number of gases that have been implicated. The direct release of heat by human activity amounts to less than 1/20,000 of the energy received from the sun. With the exception of microclimates associated with cities the effect of direct heating on global temperatures is of no consequence.

3.14. Reduction of carbon dioxide emissions depends wholly on the reduction of the usage of fossil fuels. The options are:

(a) energy is produced in a usable form with greater efficiency

(b) sources of energy are chosen so as to reduce carbon dioxide emissions, including the use of non fossil fuel sources of energy

(c) less energy is used, either by accepting lower living standards, or implementing conservation measures.

3.15. In the UK the origins of carbon dioxide are distributed over a number of different sectors (Table 3.8). Power stations contribute one-third of the total. This reflects the dependence upon the use of coal in electricity generation. The other sectors tend to use petroleum or natural gas, fuels which have a lower carbon content than coal. Together fossil fuel sources account for around 90% of the total energy used in the UK.

3.16. The use of a fossil fuel involves firstly burning the fuel and then extracting as much of the heat available from the resulting hot gases before they are released into the atmosphere. Steam represents a major portion of the exhaust gas from a boiler. Valuable heat can be obtained by allowing the steam to condense. Domestic condensing boilers are commercially available to run on gas and oil. They are more expensive than conventional boilers. In larger scale applications the possibilities are more restricted owing to the increased sulphur content of the fuels which are used, which condenses to form corrosive sulphuric acid.

3.17. Whereas direct use of the energy as heat can be carried out with high efficiency, conversion into an intermediate form involves major losses of energy. The efficiency of conversion of heat energy into motion or electricity is governed by laws of thermodynamics, and the efficiency is determined by the temperature difference between the temperature of the heat source and the temperature of the heat sink. Efficiencies in excess of around 30% are hard to achieve. Once converted into electricity further conversion can be achieved normally at very high efficiencies. There are three ways of making the conversion of energy more efficient:

(a) Increase the temperature of the heat source - burn the fuel at a higher temperature. It should be noted that increased temperatures increase the formation of nitrogen oxides which are linked to acid rain.

(b) Reduce the temperature of the heat rejected.

(c) Find a use for the heat rejected, e.g. district heating.

3.18. Car engines running on petroleum are very inefficient at part load. Marginal improvements have been obtained by the use of fuel injection and electronic engine management systems. Lean burn technology reduces fuel consumption by 10 to 15% and significantly reduces emissions of NO_x and CO. Three-way catalytic converters

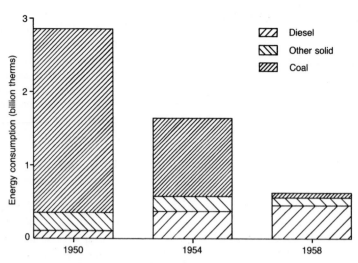

Figure 3.1. Energy consumption by UK railways (transition from coal to oil). Source: Department of Energy

reduce emissions of NO_x and CO further, but with the penalty of increased fuel consumption of around 5%. In the longer term research on the development of direct injection systems for petrol engines may allow efficiencies to approach those of current diesel engines.

Table 3.11. Fuel into motion

	Efficiency
Steam engine	10%
Car engine	18-25%
Diesel engine	30-40%
Gas turbine	<34%

3.19. Diesel engines are inherently more efficient than petrol engines, but are more expensive. The introduction of turbocharging has improved efficiencies. In the longer term there is the prospect of the 'adiabatic diesel', which by use of ceramic components can run at much higher temperatures and therefore more efficiently than conventional engines. In urban motoring the fuel consumption of a diesel engine may be only two-thirds of that of a petrol engine, although at motorway speeds, the advantage of a diesel engine over petrol is reduced. Diesel engines are noisier than petrol and can emit smoke which is carcinogenic. Despite the greater efficiency of the diesel engine it is regarded by the public as being generally dirtier than petrol engines because the pollution it produces is visible, and audible. Smoke emissions can be minimised by regular maintenance - correct atomisation, mixture adjustment and injection timing. Techniques have been established to reduce smoke emission and lorries are now commercially available in the UK, but further development is needed. On balance, adoption of diesel engines in cars should be encouraged.

3.20. The efficiency of gas turbines, which are used both for powering aircraft and small power stations has improved progressively since their invention. Gas turbines improve in efficiency with increasing size, and this is reflected in the move towards the production of larger and more powerful engines. Experiments are underway with ceramic and monolithic turbine blades which would allow greater thermal efficiencies and higher power to weight ratios.

3.21. The transition from coal to oil power on British Rail is an excellent example of the savings in energy that can be made by improving thermal efficiency. Figure 3.1 shows how energy consumption on British Rail plummeted over just eight years by replacing steam locomotives (efficiency under 10%) with diesel (efficiency over 30%).

Electricity

3.22. Developments in power station technology are enabling conversion efficiencies to reach 50%. Power is obtained initially by burning the fuel to drive a gas turbine connected to an electrical generator, and in

Table 3.12. Fuel into electricity

	Efficiency
Older type power station	30%
Modern power station	38%
New technology combined cycle power station	40-50%

addition the hot exhaust is then used to generate steam which drives a steam turbine. Measures which will enable power to be generated at higher temperatures are continuously being sought.

3.23. The options for reducing the temperature of the waste heat generated in producing electricity by power stations have already been taken up. For example the final condensing stages of steam turbines in large power stations are barely above atmospheric temperature at around 30°C.

Heat pumps

3.24. Engines work by taking heat and using it to produce motion. The process can work in the opposite direction. Energy, in the form of motion, can be used through an engine to provide valuable heat. The technology is widespread and most homes in the UK are equipped with heat pumps which are commonly known as a refrigerators. Most refrigerators use electrical energy to drive a compressor which pumps heat out of the cabinet and releases it into the room. Heat pumps are also available to provide space and water heating. Heat is extracted from the air or ground or nearby lakes or rivers and used to heat buildings. Provided the temperature difference between the source of the heat and the output is kept small, the total heat output can be several times in excess of the electrical energy input. Because heat pumps are expensive the payback period is long, and as a result they have not been widely adopted. In addition, the working fluids used in heat pumps and refrigerators give off gases which affect the ozone layer.

Using the waste heat - combined heat and power

3.25. District heating schemes offer a potential use for the waste heat resulting from the generation of electricity by power stations. Hot water used in the cooling process is fed from power stations to cities and towns, and may then be used to heat buildings. District heating schemes operate in Scandinavia but are not widely used in the UK. There are a number of problems:

(a) An extensive distribution piping network is required to service offices, factories and domestic houses. The depths below urban streets are already crowded with sewers, water pipes, electricity cables, telephone cables, gas mains and increasingly cable television fibre optics. An additional network of hot pipes are difficult to accommodate, and expensive to install.

(b) Most power stations in the UK are sited near coal fields and oil terminals rather than centres of population,

(c) The waste heat from UK power stations is around 30C which is too cold for use even in domestic heating where 60C is the minimum required.

As a result, the prospects for large-scale CHP in the short and medium term are small. The present practice in the UK is to generate electricity in large centralised power stations and supply heat in small localised boilers. The efficiency of providing heat locally compensates for the inefficiency of central electricity generation and the losses that would occur in distributing the heat. While there is little likelihood of existing cities being 'converted' to CHP, there is more scope in new developments. The East Midlands case study illustrates the potential for the construction of a small power station in Leicester connected into a district heating scheme.

3.26. CHP is also available on a small scale using internal combustion engines fired on gas. While there are many suitable applications including municipal buildings, leisure centres etc, the uptake has been slow. Since the early 1980s the price of energy has been comparatively low and this may have reduced the impetus towards projects. A further problem may have been the capital constraints placed on local authorities which have restricted funding of CHP schemes, whether financed directly by the local authority or contracted on a leasing basis through an energy management company (regarded by the Treasury as 'unconventional finance'). In the circumstance that energy conservation will attract increasing emphasis, CHP schemes should be encouraged.

Reducing the demand
Energy in buildings

3.27. There are many opportunities to reduce the energy used in buildings, both existing and built in the future, even though some of the more capital intensive measures proposed have a long pay-back. The average occupancy of a house in the UK is around seven years. Consequently the owner of the house may not even recover the initial investment on conservation measures, unless reflected in a higher sale price. The latter is subject to variations which depend on the wider general market.

3.28. Central heating systems can ensure that over 80% of the heat available from the fuel burnt is released into a building, but there is no guarantee that the heat will remain. However, it is now possible to design buildings which use a fraction of the heat used by conventional buildings by good insulation, and the use of energy management and heat recovery techniques.

Insulation

3.29. While cavity wall insulation can be applied to many of the buildings constructed since the 1930s, a large proportion of the housing stock possesses solid brick walls and the only method of insulation is to use internal or external cladding. Internal cladding reduces the interior space, external cladding entirely alters the appearance of houses. Cladding is also expensive. Insulation under pitched roofs produces a rapid payback. Minimum standards for roof insulation are laid down in the building regulations, but a large proportion of the existing housing stock has not been treated.

Table 3.13. U values - a measure of heat loss (W/m^2 per °C temperature difference)

Walls

Typical solid brick wall	1.90
Solid wall plus external/internal insulation board	0.86
Cavity wall	1.50
Insulated cavity wall	0.55

Roofs

Typical pitched roof	2.50
Pitched roof + 100mm glass wool insulation	0.31

Glazing

Single	5.60
Double	2.80
Triple	1.90

Source: Energy Management, Murphy and McKay

Control systems

3.30. Modern electronic control technology can provide significant reductions in energy consumption. 'Optimum start control' of heating aims to ensure that the boilers are turned on at the last possible moment to achieve the required temperature at the time when the building is due to be occupied. Such systems can reduce heating bills by 25 to 40%. Fitting thermostats to radiators and hot water cylinders in the home also offer valuable energy savings.

Lighting

3.31. In the commercial sector lighting is a major consumer of energy and can account for almost half the total use of energy in an office. The problem of commercial offices has tended to become what to do with excess heat arising from direct solar gain, artificial lighting and the growing array of electronic office equipment. Dependence on natural lighting can result in high levels of solar gain in summer and excessive heat loss in winter, but careful design of new buildings can optimise the heat gain from the low winter sun without causing overheating in the summer. Double glazing cuts heat loss by one half but has a long pay back period, typically over ten years. Coated glasses are commercially available which control the amount of heat lost or admitted and offer further savings in energy. The more extensive use of low energy lighting could also contribute to savings.

Ventilation

3.32. The past decade has seen the emergence of 'sick building syndrome' associated with artificial ventilation. There is also the danger from radon gas in certain geological areas, where ventilation rates are drastically reduced. Caution has to be exercised in constructing energy efficient buildings which provide a comfortable, attractive and healthy environment. Using modern heat exchangers to combine a high ventilation rate and minimum use of heat, further energy savings can be achieved.

3.33. Housing tends to have a long lifetime - in the order of 100 years. Much of the housing stock in the UK was built when energy use was not a material consideration, or when people would accept lower standards of heating. There is a need to reduce the energy consumption of the present building stock.

3.34. Energy conservation measures available for buildings offer excellent rates of return, but uptake is still slow. Government education campaigns in the past have had little effect. In the commercial sector energy usage is not normally at the head of the list of costs, and attracts little attention from management. There is a need to raise the importance and the cost effectiveness of energy conservation methods in the view of the public. The recognition of the function of energy managers within the management structure should be given active consideration by a wider range of organisations.

Energy in industry

3.35. The key to the reduction of energy consumption in industry is good housekeeping and attention to detail. It is vital to keep insulation in good repair and to ensure that plant is not used unnecessarily and to ensure that materials which require to be heated for successive processes are not left to cool in the interim. There is often scope for the recovery of waste heat from processes and a wide range of different technologies are available for this purpose.

Energy in motion

3.36. The more extensive use of public transport can make a substantial contribution to energy conservation. Used to capacity, public transport can be ten times more energy efficient than the private motor car. In transporting freight, rail based systems are over four times more energy efficient.

3.37. The fuel economy of road transport systems has improved since the 1970s oil crisis. Energy losses arise from rolling resistance, wind resistance, and losses from braking. Measures available include modifications to tyres to reduce rolling resistance, improvements to aerodynamics to reduce drag (but this becomes significant only at speeds above 30mph), and reduction in weight to reduce braking losses. In the USA there has been a move towards the use of smaller cars coupled with a speed limit of 55mph which together have had a significant impact on energy use. Improvements to infrastructure can reduce the requirement for vehicles to make intermittent stops e.g. phased traffic lights etc. Regenerative braking systems offer potential savings but the technology has not been widely deployed, even on electric railway systems where there is greatest scope.

3.38. In the United Kingdom it is the transport sector which is increasing in its energy consumption at the greatest rate, and this is a reflection of the increase in vehicle distances travelled. The National Travel Survey suggests that much of the increased distance travelled by private motorists is due to people making longer journeys -particularly to and from work. Workers are commuting at ever increasing distances, and any attempt to stem the rise in energy consumption of private motorists must take this into account.

Restructuring - finding other sources of energy

3.39. Given the world's almost total dependence on fossil fuels, a change to the use of alternative sources would take decades to achieve and would require a revolution in practise. There is no single energy technology that could replace fossil fuels. However there are a number of different technologies in various stages of development which in combination can make a contribution to solving the problem.

Fuel switching

3.40. Substituting fuels which are high in carbon content by others which are rich in hydrogen offers the prospect of an immediate reduction in the levels of carbon dioxide produced by coal fired plant.

Table 3.14. Properties of selected fuels

	Calorific value $J10^6$/kg	Carbon hydrogen ratio	Sulphur content %
Natural gas	50	3.1	Trace
Diesel	43	6.4	0.7
Heavy oil	40	7.7	3.5
Wood	14	6.2	0.8
Peat	14	6.8	1.5
Coals			
Bituminous	32	15.1	2.3
Anthracitic	33	30.1	1.4

Source: Energy Management, Murphy and McKay

3.41. Table 3.14 shows how the carbon content of fossil fuels varies. Anthracitic coal is rich in carbon, bituminous coals and oil contain progressively greater proportions of hydrogen which burns to form water (H_2O). Carbon dioxide emissions may therefore be reduced by switching from coal to oil. The potential for fuel switching is shown in Table 3.15. During the miners' strike the CEGB were obliged to switch from coal to oil-burning power stations. In consequence the consumption of oil dramatically increased but the output of carbon dioxide fell by 10%. The ability of the CEGB to do this was based on having a diversity of potential power sources to meet different circumstances.

3.42. The problems of sulphur tend also to be associated with specific fuels. Heavy oils and coal are high in sulphur - though there is much variation between sources. Natural gas, light oils and petrol are low in sulphur.

Energy in the right form

3.43. A problem of many of the alternative power sources is that the energy comes in the form of electricity. A sizeable portion of the world's energy consumption is in transportation. Electricity is not well suited to powering cars or lorries, nor ships, save a handful of nuclear powered vessels. It is also not energy efficient in the sense that the recharging of batteries makes high energy demands. Battery cars are being developed which will make electric road transport viable (an 100mph version is under test) but a production model is some years away. Widespread use of electric power will depend on the development of high performance fuel cells. Schemes have been put forward for the conversion of nuclear electricity into hydrogen by the electrolysis of water. The energy to weight ratio would permit use in aircraft, but hydrogen has only one-third the calorific value of petroleum by volume, and its temperature, which approaches absolute zero, poses soluble but expensive storage problems. Whereas natural gas is combustible under only a small variation of air to fuel ratios, hydrogen burns with a high flame speed and under a wide range of conditions and is therefore more

Table 3.15. Carbon dioxide emissions

	Million tonnes	
	1984	1986
Solid fuel	55	79
Petrol	18	19
DERV	6	7
Other	36	23
Gas	30	33
Total	**145**	**161**

Source: H.S. Eggleston, Warren Spring Laboratory, unpublished work.

dangerous. Cars are being produced which run on hydrogen but much more work needs to be done to produce an efficient and safe alternative fuel for transport. The advantages of this method is that the exhaust gases produced are water vapour.

3.44. While electricity may as yet be disadvantaged as a power source for transportation, recent advances in high temperature superconductors hold out the possibility that in the distant future it may be possible to transmit electricity at negligible power loss.

Nuclear power

3.45. The technology used in conventional nuclear power stations is well tested and proven. The recent estimates of the cost of nuclear power suggest that it is more expensive than fossil fuel generation. The first generation of UK reactors, the Magnox, were an outstanding success, the second generation, the advanced gas reactor (AGR) failed to capitalise on the initial advances. Whereas the Magnox reactors were fairly closely related to a single design, there was much variation between the designs of the AGRs. The most recent AGR units constructed have performed well. There are clearly economies to be obtained by standardisation of design. Modern electronics and design could be used to make the reactors safer in operation and easier to control. Nuclear power for whatever reason has become stigmatised and has lost popular support in recent years. In addition, the fact that plutonium can be produced as a byproduct calls into question whether it is an appropriate source of power for countries which are politically unstable.

3.46. Conventional reactors use uranium 235, which is comparatively scarce and makes up only around 0.7% of the uranium which is obtained from natural sources, the remainder being uranium 238. World reserves of uranium 235 are, in available energy terms, comparable in magnitude with those of oil, and in consequence there can be no prospect of conventional nuclear power taking over as the world's primary source of energy. Fast breeder reactors can generate fuel from the more abundant uranium 238 which can be reprocessed and used in other reactors. They utilise over 60 times more of the energy available in natural uranium than conventional reactors. There is, however, a limit to the rate at which a fast breeder reactor programme could be built up which is governed by the rate at which new fuel can be generated and reprocessed. There are large stocks of plutonium and uranium 238 which could be used to fuel a fast breeder programme held in the world's nuclear weapons arsenal. Fast breeder reactor technology could provide a very major contribution to the world's energy needs in the next century.

Nuclear fusion

3.47. The fuel for fusion reactors is obtained from sea water in abundance. It is estimated that there is sufficient recoverable to meet all the world's current energy needs for over 3,000 years. There have been periodic false reports concerning fusion. Britain claimed a breakthrough in the 1950s with its Zeta programme and in 1989 there were claims that a technique for cold fusion had been discovered. Regrettably these claims were unfounded. To achieve the conditions necessary for fusion requires immense temperatures and pressures. There are two main lines of research. In the USA the technique has been to use inertial confinement, using the concentrated beams from powerful lasers to compress and heat matter. In Europe and the USSR experiments have been undertaken in magnetic confinement. The Joint European Torus at Culham in England has achieved excellent results in approaching the necessary conditions. A working fusion reactor is decades away, but it is of vital importance that research in this field should be continuously supported.

Decommissioning

3.48.   All power plant has a finite life expectation. Materials corrode, insulation becomes defective, bearings wear and the burden of maintenance increases to a point at which it is cheaper to build a new installation. At this point there arises the problem of what to do with the redundant structure.   In the case of conventional power stations the problem is solved by demolition or re-equipment.   Certain components within nuclear power stations become radioactive through continuous exposure over the life of the reactor.   The radioactivity takes a long time to subside - measured in many years.   The cost of decommissioning a nuclear reactor is dependent on the extent to which the site is required to be restored.   Restoration to greenfield site involves removal of all the contaminated components to a special disposal site.   The cost of this operation is phenomenally expensive and of dubious benefit - one site is decontaminated at the expense of the contamination of a different site.   A compromise is needed.   The bulk of the site buildings and generation equipment which are never exposed to radiation can be demolished using conventional techniques. The radioactive portions of the structure (the reactor vessel and primary heat exchangers) may be isolated in additional concrete shielding, mounded over and then left over the ensuing years for the radioactivity to subside.

Nuclear waste

3.49.   The main components of nuclear radiation are gamma radiation, which is a very energetic form of electromagnetic radiation, and a series of particles which are emitted at a high velocity by decaying atoms, including beta, alpha and neutron radiation.   The process of radiation damage involves breaking of molecular bonds, damage to genetic material or crystal structure which may lead for example to steels becoming brittle.   Beta and alpha radiation are ineffective at penetrating matter. Although easy to shield, this radiation is dangerous in that damage is localised and intense. Neutron and gamma radiation interact with matter far less strongly and in consequence thick shielding is required, and damage tends to be dispersed through the material. There is no question that nuclear radiation is dangerous. Fatalities arise as a consequence of excessive exposure. However radiation is used for medical purposes.   It is also true that the risk from that radiation can be controlled.   The actual hazard presented is very small compared to other risks in society.   Driving cars is a dangerous activity killing 5,000 and injuring 320,000 per annum in the UK.   Yet society accepts this carnage - equivalent to six Falklands wars each year.   Death due to diseases of the circulatory system accounted for 306,000 in 1988, and diseases of the respiratory tract a further 40,000.   Many of these deaths were due to avoidable factors such as smoking and diet.   Faced with these avoidable risks society opts not to avoid them.   Balanced judgement suggests that nuclear power cannot be eliminated on safety and will have a vital contribution to make to future energy supplies.

3.50.   Nuclear radiation hazard occurs in the following forms:

(a)   disposal of spent fuel
(b)   emission during power station operation
(c)   power station failure e.g. Chernobyl
(d)   emission during reprocessing.

3.51.   Nuclear power stations in regular operation emit very little radioactivity.   The major reactor failure in recent years was at Chernobyl, which dispersed radioactive materials over a wide area. The lesser impact of the Three Mile Island failure was due to a different and safer reactor design and the enclosure of the reactor within a containment vessel.   This greatly lessened the dispersion of radioactive

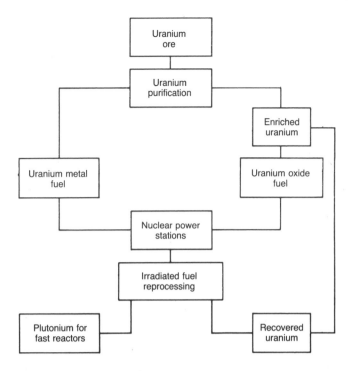

Figure 3.2. The nuclear fuel cycle.

particles. The number of fatalities in the UK in consequence of the accident is anticipated to be just over one per year over the next thirty years. Deaths arising from the use of coal are many times this number both through accidents in coal mining and transportation, and in respiratory illness of the general population. The environmental consequences of oil spillage are well known, in European seas with the Torey Canyon and Amoco Cadis disasters and recently in Alaska. The bulk of radioactive emissions occurs during fuel fabrication and reprocessing. After a poor start, mostly at one site, Sellafield, the levels of emissions from UK reprocessing plant are now very low. Figure 3.2 shows the nuclear fuel cycle. The establishment of a clean and well regulated nuclear reprocessing facility is the key to the long term prospects of nuclear power.

3.52. Disposal of nuclear waste is defined into three categories: High level, medium level, and low level. "Statistically safe" (but not politically safe) means of storage are available for all forms of nuclear waste. There is often much concern over the problem of disposal of high level waste. The volume of high level waste resulting from thirty years of nuclear power in the UK amounts to no more than the equivalent of two semi detached houses. A vitrification plant is due to come into operation during the 1990s which will convert high level waste into a stable solid form which can be handled more easily while the radioactivity subsides.

3.53. The Nuclear Industry Radioactive Waste Executive (NIREX) have put forward several types of proposals for the construction of underground waste disposal sites for low level and intermediate wastes. Most recently sites constructed several thousand metres under the surface, which would enable any nuclear waste to be totally isolated, are being investigated. Local objections have hitherto obstructed the development of a safe repository.

Alternative energy systems

3.54. There are two principal difficulties common to the majority of sources of alternative energy:

Table 3.16. *Costs of alternative energy sources*

Source	Cost pence per kWh	Potential % of UK energy demand
Wind power		
Onshore	2.0 - 3.0	20
Offshore	3.5 - 8.1	100
Tidal power	6.0 - 16.0	16
Wave power	4.0 - 16.0	25
Biomass		12

Source: House of Lords Energy Sub-Committee report on Alternative Energy.

Tidal power

(a) The initial capital investment is high and the returns while small on an annual basis proceed far into the future. Alternative energy sources are thus critically dependent on the investment criteria chosen.

(b) Few of the alternative energy sources provide a 'firm' source of power. A coal-fired power station, or a domestic central heating system can be turned on and off at will. There is no control over the availability of some of the solar derived sources:

(i) Wind correlates well with energy demand - when the weather is worst there is ample energy available. However still, frosty weather finds wind power wanting.

(ii) Wave power is similarly disposed, though ocean waves tend to be a more reliable source of energy than the wind but less controllable.

(iii) The availability of tidal power is determined by predictable lunar and daily cycles.

(iv) Solar power is subject to annual and daily cycles - it correlates inversely with energy demand.

3.55. UK demand for energy cannot be controlled over the short term, that is on a minute by minute or even hour by hour basis. The supply of energy has to be matched to meet the demand. Alternative energy sources are to a large extent fixed - either energy must be stored, alternative power supplies made available to make good the shortfall, or demand adjusted to meet the supply. Several major pumped storage schemes are in operation in Wales and Scotland, which store surplus energy and release it at times of demand, but they can only deal with short term fluctuations. The cost of using alternative energy sources must be measured by not only taking into account their own cost but also taking into account the cost of maintaining additional sources of energy in reserve so that a reliable supply of energy can be maintained.

3.56. The UK is exceptionally well placed to utilise many of the alternative energy forms including tidal, wind, wave and hydro energy, and to a lesser degree biomass and solar energy.

3.57. There are a number of schemes already in operation including La Rance in Brittany, in Canada and the USSR. The United Kingdom is well favoured to use tidal power having a number of sites which offer high tidal ranges. The technology is well tried and tested. Schemes have been put forward for the Mersey and the Severn Estuary

3.58. The Severn Estuary has the second highest tidal range in the world and is the UK's largest source of alternative energy from a single site. The Severn Barrage would contribute up to 7% of the country's electrical power needs and would also offer a third crossing of the Severn into Wales, and improved recreational use of the Severn Estuary. The main problem is that the financial return of the project is low, in the order of 5% on the capital investment. Its construction has to be weighed against the considerable benefit of future generations and a major revitalisation of the Severn Estuary for leisure and light industry. The Severn Barrage will alter the appearance of the Severn Estuary. Some of the changes may be detrimental. The Severn is an important feeding area for migratory birds and it has been suggested that the reduction of the tidal range will reduce the availability of mud flats, and one species could be affected. It has also been suggested that the barrage will entrap pollutants. Studies suggest that neither of these suggestions would materialise.

3.59. The Severn has the appearance of being a very muddy estuary.

It is not. The majority of the estuary bottom is exposed rock or clay and the muddy appearance is because the exceptionally rapid flow of water keeps in suspension particles of mud and sand which would otherwise settle to the bottom. The effect of the barrage will be to reduce velocities and the water will become clear. The present high level of particles in suspension in the water and the very fast currents have a retrograde effect on the growth of marine life and it is anticipated that food supplies for migratory birds will increase with the construction of the barrage. The configuration of the sluices and the turbines is designed so as to encourage the circulation of water, the effect, rather than to trap pollutants will be to increase the mixing of salt and fresh water so that salinity in the upper reaches of the estuary is expected to rise in relation to present levels.

3.60. The Mersey Barrage is one-tenth of the scale of the Severn Barrage, with a capacity of 700MW. The mud banks which are the winter feeding grounds of the migrating waders are least affected by the increased water levels behind the Barrage. Oxygen levels will improve with impoundment and effluent treatment which is already under way. Regeneration of Merseyside by tourism and other development should follow. The Barrage is estimated to generate energy for 120 years.

Wind energy

3.61. Wind energy has been harnessed over many centuries and the traditional windmill was for many years one of the few available sources of energy. The advent of steam and the internal combustion engine has reduced its importance. But wind turbines producing effective power have been developed in many countries and are now in operation.

3.62. In the UK, the best wind sites are normally in coastal regions where the population is less dense and there would be no interface with farming. They cause no pollution except from an aesthetic point of view and some noise. The careful selection of wind farm sites will ensure that these factors are mitigated. Over the last seven years in the UK, demonstration wind turbines up to 3MW have been successfully operated and necessary technical development has been achieved. A series of wind farm sites have been selected and are likely to be built as part of the non fossil fuel option. Much progress has been made in Europe, in Denmark 2,000 wind turbines are producing 200MW of power. In the US, over 1,500MW of capacity is now installed.

3.63. The growth of wind power can be progressively expanded and it can play an increasing role in reducing pollution by replacing the use of fossil fuels.

Wave power

3.64. A number of demonstration devices are in existence including the Wave Contouring Raft and the Oscillating Water Column. The inherent problem with wave power is the exceptionally violent nature of the sea. Wave heights off the Atlantic coast reach 20 metres, and wave power devices must be able to survive in these conditions with a factor of safety in reserve. Assessments differ on the practicality of wave power devices; there is abundant energy available, but the question whether that energy can be reliably and cheaply harnessed remains unanswered. Further research in this area is urgently required.

Hydro power

3.65. Small scale power schemes have considerable potential in providing local power and even in the UK there are sufficient additional sites to increase hydroelectric generation by around 50%. Many major international hydroelectric schemes are now in operation but recently schemes, e.g. on the Danube, in New Zealand and Brazil, have encountered objections in terms of direct environmental damage and serious environmental consequences including pollution, increased disease, disruption of agriculture by the interruption of sediment flows, and an increased risk from localised ground movements. The assessment of advantages from large schemes needs much wider and more vigorous consideration.

Biomass

3.66. Energy obtained from crops, trees and organic waste. Third World countries are to a great degree dependent on this form of solar energy, though the efficiency of conversion is very low - below 1%. However the technology is undeniably easy to apply in Third World countries and the use of appropriate technology could achieve better use of the resources. Biomass should only be pursued on a recyclable basis, lest over exploitation should alter the ecological balance. History abounds with examples of over cultivation, such as the deforestation of Mediterranean islands, the dustbowl of the 1930s America, and more recently the destruction of the rain forest and the southward progression of the Sahara Desert.

3.67. In the United Kingdom biomass has a potentially important role to play. There are two sources: firstly from refuse and sewage and secondly from 'energy crops'. DoE estimates suggest that 5Mtoe is buried annually in municipal refuse tips, 25% of which could be economically converted into useful energy. Anaerobic digestion of sewage sludge and refuse produces methane which can be used to generate electricity. Proposals have recently been put forward by the Nature Conservancy Council for the creation of five national forests in the Midlands on derelict urban and under utilised agricultural land. Biomass is unique in that it is the one alternative energy source which has been used successfully for modern transport. Alcohol-based fuels can be produced by fermentation, and are suitable for use in cars. Brazil has been the leading example though it is understood that the system is now winding down. The cost of production is not economic in European countries at current fuel prices.

3.68. It has been estimated that biomass could contribute several per cent of the UK's current energy needs. Funding of research has been limited, and it is clear that more attention should be directed to this area in anticipation of increasing costs and diminishing supplies of fossil fuels

Solar energy

3.69. The sun provides the earth's most abundant power source. The intensity of the radiation at the edge of the earth's atmosphere is 1.353 kW/m^2. The atmosphere absorbs some of the energy but on the earth's surface intensity can still be well above $1kW/m^2$ on a clear day.

3.70. Passive solar.   Through designing buildings to make the most of the sun's energy and incorporating good insulation, domestic heating requirements can be reduced by as much as 75% as against a conventionally designed building. Owing to the long lifespan of housing of 100 years and more the implementation of such techniques are likely to be slow. However there is scope for retrofitting and savings of 25% have been claimed.

3.71. Active solar - thermal. The economics for this form of solar heating are very poor in the UK. The supply of energy is at its least when it is most needed. High efficiency solar collectors are required to produce heat in winter conditions. They are expensive and the amount of heat available on an overcast winter day may be as little as $60W/m^2$. Solar heating is better suited for swimming pools which are used mainly in the summer.

3.72. Active solar - photovoltaic. Solar energy can be converted directly into electricity at efficiencies of up to 13%. Amorphous silicon cells represent the most cost effective conversion system as yet devised, but these have still to be proved competitive. There is the possibility of using desert areas for solar farms, in which energy could be transmitted by cable or converted into hydrogen for later use.

Geothermal

3.73. A research project has been operating in the UK at Cambourne for a number of years. While vast amounts of heat are retained in the earth's crust, it is difficult to get at. Deep drilling is required and the cost of drilling increases disproportionately with depth. Successful geothermal projects are operating in Europe and overseas.

Acid rain and smog

3.74. There is now little doubt that acid rain arising from the combustion of fossil fuels is causing significant damage to plant life in Western Europe and contributing to the acidification of lakes. Recent evidence has suggested that England itself is experiencing damage to trees on a wide scale. In addition the occurrence of photochemical smog is increasing in some countries.

Ozone

3.75. In the stratosphere the presence of ozone is essential. It shields the earth's surface from ultra violet radiation from the sun. The destruction of the stratospheric ozone layer is a current cause for concern. At ground level, ozone damages plant and animal life, it is produced in consequence of a reaction between oxygen and nitrogen oxides generated in combustion processes, which is catalysed in the presence of sunlight. The control of surface level ozone rests on the control of nitrogen oxide emissions.

Nitrogen oxides (NO_x)

3.76. Nitrogen (N_2) is the main constituent of air and is also found in fuels. At room temperature nitrogen is relatively inert. At high temperatures the nitrogen reacts with atmospheric oxygen to form oxides of nitrogen. The formation of nitrogen oxides is dependent on two main conditions: the temperature of combustion, and the air to fuel ratio. In general the higher the temperature at which combustion occurs, the greater is the tendency to form nitrogen oxides. Table 3.17 shows analyses of the main sources of nitrogen oxides. The principal sources are power stations and road transport.

Table 3.17. Nitrogen oxide emissions UK - ground based sources 1986

Power stations	41%
Road transport	41%
Other industry	9%
Domestic	3%
Commercial/services	2%
Refineries	2%
Rail transport	2%

Source: DoE, 1988

3.77. The problem of nitrogen oxides should be seen against the drive towards higher thermal efficiency through higher combustion temperatures. The emission of nitrogen oxides in power stations can be moderated by careful control of the combustion conditions and it is possible to obtain improvements on existing plant. Over the next few years nitrogen oxide emissions by power stations are expected to fall considerably. The new technology of fluidised bed combustion is inherently low in emissions of nitrogen oxide.

3.78. There are two routes available for reducing the emission of nitrogen oxides by road transport, either using the high compression lean burn engines which have been developed in the UK, and three way catalytic converters which have been developed in the USA but are now available on some cars in Western Europe. The converters reduce nitrogen oxide emissions by around 80% and eliminate carbon monoxide and unoxidised hydrocarbons, but increase fuel consumption by around 5%. The high compression lean burn engines in conjunction with electronic engine management and fuel injection allow similar reductions in nitrogen oxide emission but have the added advantage of reducing fuel consumption by 10 to 15%. The additional cost on the price of the car is around £500 in both cases.

Sulphur dioxide

3.79. The emission of sulphur dioxide in combustion processes is dependent on how much sulphur is present in the fuel. The main components of fossil fuels are carbon, and hydrogen. When burnt, the end products are water and carbon dioxide. However there are also impurities in fuels including sulphur, and a trace of radioactive elements. The resulting sulphur dioxide causes acid rain.

3.80. High sulphur levels are found in the poorer grades of coal and in heavy oils - both of which are burnt mainly in large power stations. In the UK the policy has been to construct tall chimneys several hundred metres high which permit the flue gasses to be dispersed over long distances. There is very little sulphur in the fuels used by cars and lorries and in consequence their contribution to sulphur dioxide emissions is negligible in comparison.

Table 3.18. Sulphur dioxide emissions UK - ground based sources 1986

Power stations	70%
Other industry	16%
Domestic	5%
Refineries	5%
Commercial/services	4%
Road transport	1%
Agriculture	Trace

Source: DoE, 1988

3.81. Table 3.18 shows that power stations are the main source of sulphur dioxide emissions. There are two alternative options for reducing emissions, firstly to burn only that fuel which is low in sulphur, or to install equipment for removing sulphur from the fuel or the resulting flue gasses. Switching to low sulphur coal would offer a rapid solution to the problem. UK coal tends to be high in sulphur, and if it were to be replaced, coal would have to be imported, with balance of payments and employment implications for the UK mining industry.

3.82. There are techniques for removing sulphur or sulphur dioxide from flue gases which are practical but will increase the price of electricity. The main technique is to react lime with the sulphur dioxide to produce gypsum commonly used in plasterboard. Fluidised bed combustion technology is easily adapted to the removal of sulphur dioxide simply by adding lime to the bed. An alternative method of treatment is to reclaim the sulphur as a raw material. Sulphur is a potentially more valuable product than gypsum. Typically a 90% reduction in sulphur dioxide emissions can be obtained.

3.83. Flue gas desulphurisation can absorb over 7% of the output of a power station. More fuel must be burnt to produce the same amount of electricity and in consequence emissions of carbon dioxide would increase. The capital cost of the plant amounts to an additional 10% on the cost of a power station. Under present plans it is unlikely that there will be significant retrofitting of power stations with flue gas desulphurisation equipment, and the prospect is that it will be incorporated in new units. The economics of fluidised bed combustion or gasification of coal as part of a combined cycle generation plant may be more favourable, as well as offering net improvements in generation efficiency. Pilot plants have been constructed in Western Europe and there should be encouragement to build a full scale unit.

3.84. Much of the technology that is used to reduce emissions from power stations is also suitable for application in industry, the second largest source.

3.85. In practical terms, sulphur dioxide emissions is not an issue in the other sectors: domestic, commercial/service and road transport. High sulphur fuels cannot be easily used in these sectors because of the problem of corrosion.

Conclusion: The greenhouse effect

3.86. The greenhouse effect is still unproven and any measures taken at this stage should be precautionary. If a policy decision is taken to reduce the emissions of carbon dioxide then the following options are available in the short term.

(a)   Imposition of taxation on carbon based fuel sources. It should be noted however that the demand for fuel is inelastic and large increases in price would be needed to have any effect on consumption.

(b)   Power stations. Switching from coal to oil burning would achieve a 10% reduction but at increased electricity prices.

(c)   Transportation. Consideration should be given to reducing the upper speed limit for cars and to reducing the HGV speed limit to 50mph (as discussed in paragraph 4.54).

(d)   Education. A campaign to raise awareness of the importance of conserving energy.

Medium and long term

3.87. Policies aimed at reducing the impact of the greenhouse effect have much in common with policies aimed at securing energy supplies against the eventual exhaustion of fossil fuel reserves. There are three objectives

(a)   to secure new sources of energy

(b)   to reduce the level of demand for energy

(c)   to improve the efficiency of the use of existing energy resources.

3.88. Conventional nuclear power offers a relatively safe and reliable power source. The level of radiation is being progressively reduced as standards are set by Government regulations. There remains the problem of prejudice against nuclear power. Transportation and coal fired power generation are several orders of magnitude more dangerous than nuclear power, both through direct accident and through respiratory diseases. Prejudice needs to be overcome by public display of the facts.

3.89. In order to secure power supplies in the long term, the development of the technology of fast breeder reactors should be supported, with a view to the establishment of a European programme for the construction of a series of power stations. The funding must be by central government in cooperation with other countries. The UK's involvement in international research into nuclear fusion should be continued and increased.

3.90. The safety and regulation of the nuclear fuel cycle is the key to the long term success and acceptability of nuclear power. Public confidence in the monitoring of safety needs to be restored. Objections to nuclear power are often based on suspicion and mistrust. It is important that the organisation set up to monitor safety in the operation of nuclear power should be accepted by the public as being entirely independent of the industry. The Nuclear Installations Inspectorate is independent of the industry and part of the Health and Safety Executive. It is important to establish international standards for the design, operation and safety requirements of all nuclear installations.

3.91. Alternative energy sources should receive greatly increased funding from Government. Whereas the UK can rely on other countries to carry out research in solar power it should take a lead in wind, wave and tidal power development, in view of the UK's exceptional potential for the exploitation of these resources.

3.92. Conservation measures are already available which would reduce substantially the consumption of energy. A large number of these measures offer a rapid payback. Low uptake points to market inefficiency. Firms should be encouraged to appoint persons with responsibility for energy use within the organisation. Householders should be encouraged to implement measures, by low interest loans made available from government funds. A system of energy rating of housing has been introduced and should be given active support.

3.93. Financial appraisal methods in use at present, do not adequately appraise the benefits of long term investment. Benefits that arise much beyond thirty years into the future tend to be ignored. Consideration must be given to the development and use of investment appraisal techniques which do not discount long term benefits. The Severn and Mersey Barrage, projects which could provide an almost indefinite source of benign power, perform poorly under conventional appraisal techniques.

Free market solution

3.94. The problems of the greenhouse effect and the depletion of fossil fuels are problems of future generations. There is no market solution because the market is concerned overwhelmingly with short term considerations. The failure to take up profitable energy conservation investments points to the necessity for Government intervention.

Free market and intervention

3.95. The demand for energy is insensitive to changes in price in the short term. Though large increases in the price of fuel are required to produce a change in demand, small increases in price are sufficient to encourage the development of alternative energy sources. An increased price of fuel would improve the competitiveness of alternate energy technologies and act as an incentive to development.

3.96. By raising the price of energy consumers will be encouraged to implement conservation measures and a market will be created for energy conservation products. This is likely to be a secondary effect unless supported by fiscal inducements.

A role for Government

3.97. The high cost of programmes, such as fusion research, with benefits many decades in the future, suggests that they can only be financed by the public sector. The responsibility for the long term development of alternative energy sources lies with Government.

Acid rain

3.98. There is now little doubt that acid rain is causing extensive environmental damage. While it is possible to treat some of the symptoms such as the acidification of lakes by the addition of lime, such treatment is expensive and unreliable. There is no long run alternative other than the reduction of sulphur and nitrogen oxide emissions.

3.99. The problem of sulphur dioxide emissions can be solved at additional cost. It requires the fitting and retrofitting of power stations with flue gas desulphurisation equipment or the substitution of low sulphur fuels.

3.100. Nitrogen oxides arise from road transport and power station emissions. They can be controlled in the former by the use of high compression lean burn combustion engines or catalytic converters. The technology is available. In power stations emissions can be reduced by alterations to combustion conditions.

4.   Transport

Introduction

4.1.   Transport is an economic generator of profound importance. It is a major polluter. In nearly all its forms it consumes fossil fuels, either directly or indirectly, and is responsible for significant damage to the environment. It contributes to air pollution which broadly includes the greenhouse gases, acid rain deposition, toxic gases and traffic fumes.

4.2.   The reaction to these issues in the UK lacks form and coherence. There are no national policies or limits for atmospheric pollution or environmental disbenefits which could set a framework within which development of the transport infrastructure could be assessed. Some impressive improvements have been achieved, such as the reduction of lead emissions by reducing the cost of unleaded petrol. Improvements will also result from the implementation of internationally agreed regulations such as the introduction of catalytic converters and 'lean burn' engines.

4.3.   The Government is now introducing or studying a series of measures calculated to reduce or contain environmental damage, but these measures fall well short of those needed to make really significant advances. The UK has now agreed in principle to produce a national strategy for controlling emisisons of carbon dioxide before the end of the World Climate Conference in November, as recommended by the Intergovernmental Panel on Climate Change.

4.4.   Atmospheric pollution is mainly a consequence of fossil fuel consumption, and transport as a key consumer of energy in the UK (using about 30% of all energy consumed and over 70% of petroleum) is a major polluter. Of the atmospheric pollution associated with transport, by far the biggest generator is road transport, particularly of the greenhouse gases and the various nitrogen oxides (NO_x) which contribute to acid rain (these trends are discussed in greater depth in Annex 4.B). Growth in demand for road transport is expected to continue well into the next century with current official forecasts suggesting that vehicle kilometres could double over the next 30 - 40 years (Annex 4.A) No provision is made in planning procedures for a slowing down in the rate of growth of road traffic as the road system reaches saturation point on many key sections.

4.5.   Road transport growth is still in its infancy in most of the less developed countries of the world. Starting from such a low base, the long term potential for growth of road transport in these nations is enormous and the need to accommodate this demand for mobility, without at the same time jeopardizing the atmosphere and ecosystems of the planet, is likely to pose one of the most difficult challenges society has to face.

Environmental disbenefits

4.6.   Apart from noise levels, few thresholds of acceptability are defined for environmental disbenefits of transportation, either in construction or in use. Communities normally strike some sort of balance between the benefits and disbenefits of transport as cases arise. Governments, however, with their wider interest, frequently see different balances. Whilst there is widespread unease about these issues, there is no independent UK environmental protection agency which can assess the relevant issues within a framework of national aims and objectives.

Noise

4.7.   It is almost certain within recent years that any major proposal for transport infrastructure such as new railway lines, new roads or widening works, major construction at airports or increases in capacity of docks, will meet determined opposition from local residents as well as environmental pressure groups. The main protests centre on visual intrusion, community severance, noise and ecological impact. This is of particular importance where the national interest is in conflict with local interests. For instance the need for fast rail links to the Channel Tunnel which would reduce road congestion, provide environmental improvements elsewhere and bring significant economic benefits to the nation and particularly northern industry, are not the main interest of a house owner who fears that the new lines will run close to his property.   It is essential therefore that the nature and extent of environmental disbenefits are fully understood and that a framework of evaluation is developed which will allow balanced judgements to be made between competing interests. The case studies include a number of examples of new road constructions which outline environmental considerations.

4.8.   Most forms of transport create noise. Noise from road, rail and air transport is a major source of public concern. Fear of noise pollution is one of the most persistent causes of public opposition to new transport infrastructure. As with other environmental disbenefits, there are no absolute measurements of disturbance from noise. The Land Compensation Act, 1973 provides for the payment of compensation (or noise insulation measures) when new transport infrastructure creates noise intrusion. In practice, however, the Noise Insulation Regulations made under the Act define the noise threshold above which compensation is payable only for new road construction. No equivalent frameworks for compensation are operative for rail or air.   There are extensive and complex regulations limiting noise emisisons at source from road vehicles and aircraft.

4.9.   Individuals differ in their reactions to noise emissions from different sources and this causes differences of opinion about scale. The decibel (dB) system is used as the basis of noise measurement but to determine nuisance caused by noise the A weighted scale dB(A) is used because it takes greater account of the sound frequencies at which the human ear is most sensitive. On this scale a rise of 10dB(A) represents a doubling of loudness. Whilst a rise of 3dB(A) is barely detectable to the human ear, most people can detect a change of 5dB(A).

4.10. Because transport noise is intermittent and varies in characteristics and intensity according to source, recourse is made to a variety of measurement techniques, which are considered to produce the most appropriate samples of noise disturbance. Road traffic noise is measured on the L10 scale, that is the sum of individual pulses of sound exceeded by 10% of the sample. Rail noise is measured on the Leq scale, which is an average of all individual measurements, often referred to as the 'equivalent continous sound level'. Aircraft noise is expressed as the Noise and Number Index (NNI), compiled on quite a complicated formula which allows areas around airports to be contoured to delineate areas of a similar noise exposure, although Department of Transport is now thought to favour replacement of NNI by Leq. Internationally, noise is already more commonly measured on the Leq scale.

4.11. The road traffic noise regulations fix the threshold for compensation at 68dB(A) on the L10 scale. Kent County Council propose that for rail different noise standards should apply for different times of the day, reflecting the different degrees of nuisance that are likely to be experienced. The Kent standard is mathematically equivalent to a 24 hour Leq of 63dB(A). This was adopted after extensive research and consultation, both in this country and abroad. When airport operators offered noise insulation grants in the past the base level was 50 NNI. There has been no revision of the Government's advice on compensation levels since 1973. The introduction of a revised and coherent approach to all transport induced noise is clearly overdue.

4.12. It is likely that there are many areas in the UK where people suffer greater disturbance from transport noise than should be allowed. The rate of increase in the volume of transport movements is not fully offset by the rate of reduction in noise emissions at source. When there is a substantial growth in volume due to normal growth or changes in the layout of infrastructure, the regulations make no provision for compensation because the costs are deemed to be more than society as a whole is willing to bear.

4.13. However, in the absence of relevant data it is not possible to arrive at judgements about the precise extent of unacceptable noise pollution from ground based transport sources. It is not clear that the existing statutory threshold for road schemes is generally acceptable. It is necessary, therefore, to establish the levels of transport noise which are generally unacceptable, based preferably on medical evidence. Noise contours should be plotted for existing heavily trafficked road and rail routes and merged with the NNI contours, preferably restated in Leq. On these bases, a statutory framework of acceptable noise targets could be established, for planning and development control purposes and for statutory compensation.

Vibration

4.14. Road vehicles particularly HGVs, railways and to a lesser extent aircraft on the ground produce vibrations. HGVs are free to use almost all the road system although much of it is entirely unsuitable structurally or in layout. These heavy vehicles cause vibration, which is of particular concern in small towns and villages, where old buildings and underground services may be liable to damage. Perceptible vibration from railways is almost entirely by freight trains and underground railways. Vibrations grow worse as the state of road and rail infrastructure deteriorates. The absence of any national guidelines or statutory provision for maximum acceptable levels of vibration mean that there is no reliable assessment of the scale of the problem.

Congestion

4.15. The effects of congestion in the transport system are well known and documented. Rail systems, airports and roads all suffer from congestion which is causing much concern to the public, especially in view of the forecasts of increasing road traffic and greater use of the public transport systems. The Institution of Civil Engineers published a study of the causes, effects and possible containment of congestion in 1989. The recommendations of that study, which are attracting widespread support, are compatible with this report's recommendations.

Accidents

4.16. At the present time over 5,000 people are killed and over 300,000 injured in road traffic accidents each year but these figures do not cause any widespread public outcry. With regard to accidents and safety, railways have an immense advantage over road transport. In spite of concern with standards of air transport safety, especially whenever an accident occurs, the record of the industry in these respects is very good. For the period 1977-1987 total casualties per billion passenger kilometres for air transport were 0.4 compared with figures of 70.9 for rail transport; 238 for bus and coach transport and 361 for car travel (Annex 4.F).

POLLUTION

Visual intrusion, community
severance and ecological impact

4.17. There is a growing understanding of the importance of protecting the environment in respect of visual intrusion, community severance and ecological impact. Civil engineers are now designing transportation infrastructure projects with these issues clearly in mind. However, visual intrusion involves cultural values which vary from community to community. Ecological impacts are also judged on local values although national or even international concerns may come into play. These can support or conflict with local assessments. There is no established, consistent practice by which local values can be set in a national context, nor is there any means by which the cumulative effects can be monitored.

4.18. The Standing Advisory Committee on Trunk Road Assessment has established a wide ranging assessment framework for new road schemes which includes considerations of visual intrusion, ecological impact and community severance. These are described in the Department of Transport's Manual of Environmental Appraisal. The appraisal methods, although devised for individual road schemes, have found wider, if only partial, applicability to recent proposals for new railway lines. Experience seems to indicate that the techniques employed fulfil the expectations of the EC Directive on Environmental Impact Assessment.

4.19. The methods employed by the Manual of Environmental Appraisal, however, suffer the important disadvantage that an economic appraisal of performance for individual road schemes is evaluated against an assessment of environmental impacts which are not economically appraised. The absence of a national transport plan against which schemes can be assessed raises doubts as to the effectiveness of such appraisals.

The way ahead - wider concepts

4.20. The problem with nearly all forms of environmental damage evaluation is to determine where the balance should be struck. The issues are complex and the earth is resilient. The Inter-governmental Panel on Climate Change has provisionally reported on the growing consensus among the world's scientific community on the threat of global warming. In addition, transport's contribution to overall levels of pollution and environmental damage stresses the urgent need for action on a national basis and to influence others to take action.

4.21. Public concern has now reached the stage where people are beginning to accept that measures necessary to contain environmental damage have fundamental consequences for their travel habits and expectations. This acceptance is qualified by the knowledge that whereas many environmental impacts need to be tackled on a national basis, wider issues require responses which only action by the EC, and in due course the whole world, can make effective.

4.22. In this context, the consequences of the acceptance of growth in road traffic and the attempt to provide an adequate road system for it comes into question. Society is already beginning to recognise that it cannot continue to allow unrestrained travel by road in the cities. It follows that it is not practicable to allow unrestrained travel on the inter-urban road network either, because the two cannot be separated and because there are unacceptable land use implications. It becomes clear that we must abandon the piecemeal approach to transport and land use planning. What is required is a coherent framework of national objectives within which it is possible to judge proposals.

Options for action to contain pollution
Road transport

4.23. There is now increasing evidence that

(a)   the number of cars in the UK will probably double in the foreseeable future, unless action is taken to contain the increase, and we are moving steadily towards saturation of the road system

(b)   it will not be practicable to build new roads to accommodate the probable traffic levels

(c)   we need to take all practicable steps to reduce emissions of the gases which contribute to atmospheric pollution

(d)   we need to take all practicable steps to reduce environmental damage of other forms.

It is necessary therefore to review the options for action on these assumptions, which are likely to impose their own unacceptable solutions unless firm action is taken.

4.24. Some progress has already been made in the reduction of atmospheric pollution. The introduction of legislation and tax initiatives, together with the development of more efficient engines will all serve further to reduce road transport emissions. However, if car use increases as forecast, more will have to be done.

Lead

4.25. Lead pollution by road vehicles has already been reduced by the simple expedient of lowering the tax on unleaded petrol. Some 30% of petrol is nominally lead free. Sales of unleaded petrol will gradually increase in future but this process could no doubt be speeded by increasing the tax penalty on leaded petrol further. It has been claimed that this would have doubtful results, as those who would gain financially from switching to unleaded petrol have already done so, and that reducing the price of this petrol further would encourage greater car use. The advantages of reduced lead emission at an earlier point can be held to outweigh this speculative risk, and a further small reduction of tax on unleaded petrol will hasten the process of conversion without significant adverse effects.

Carbon dioxide, carbon monoxide
hydrocarbons, nitrogen oxides

4.26. Other noxious gas emissions will be reduced over the next few years by the introduction of catalytic converters which are to be made compulsory in the EC for all new cars under 1400cc by the end of 1992. Advances will also be made through improvements in engine technology. However, the recent Worldwide Fund for Nature report on atmospheric emissions from the use of transport in the UK has come to some disturbing conclusions. It forecasts that total emissions of carbon monoxide, hydrocarbons and nitrogen oxides by road traffic will decrease steadily for about 15 years but then commence to increase again due to rising vehicle ownership and kilometres travelled. Emissions of carbon dioxide will continue to grow due to increased car usage and technologies such as catalytic converters increasing carbon dioxide emissions. Hence these are forecast to rise by around 60% on a low forecast by the year 2020 and by around 110% on a high forecast.

4.27. The introduction of catalytic converters over the years may be overtaken by advances in engine technology which are already being researched. Catalysts are not the ideal engineering solution to the problems of exhaust gases. Lean burn engines would use less fuel and thus produce less carbon dioxide. Such engines, fitted with a three way catalyst would offer significant improvement. Uncooled engines made with ceramic materials can increase combustion temperatures, which would increase efficiency and thus reduce emissions of carbon dioxide. Use of diesel engines which are more efficient than petrol engines offers improvements but this brings in the problem of particulate emissions. There are numerous other engineering developments under study, such as new types of fuel, but they all have cost penalties.

Congestion

4.28. The measures proposed in the Institution's Congestion report (1989) included road pricing, mainly aimed at the larger cities and towns, as a method of both relieving congestion and reducing car travel. However, financial measures with wider impact would also be needed to reduce road travel countrywide. There seems little doubt that if significant long term reductions are to be made in emissions, particularly of carbon dioxide, a system will have to be devised to reduce car mileage. The most appropriate means to hand for this purpose is the use of financial measures.

4.29. Car users only take into account at the time of the journey the marginal costs of car travel, i.e. the cost of petrol. Car travel is usually seen as not only more convenient but cheaper than public transport. Any measure to make the true costs more apparent must be advantageous and this would be achieved if the annual car licence tax were abolished and the equivalent costs added to the price of petrol. (This measure would have the bonus of dealing at a stroke with car owners who evade the purchase of an annual licence.)

4.30. In addition to this measure the price of petrol could be raised further. The real price of petrol is low by past standards. The Institute for Fiscal Studies has estimated that to raise prices to their peak of 1975 would need an increase in duty from the current level of 93p per gallon on four star petrol to about 148p. They further calculate that a 55p rise in duty would cut petrol consumption by nearly 8% with more reductions later as people opted for smaller cars. In this connection, the tax on new cars could be revised to favour cars with low rates of emission and penalise cars with higher rates. This would favour small cars with new technology engines and operate against large cars or those which tend to be less efficient.

4.31. The problems with increasing taxes are that

(a)   they add to inflation
(b)   they tend to hurt the poorer sections of the community more than the rich
(c)   if successful in reducing mileage the yield falls.

These factors add up to an unattractive package politically but the problems of pollution and road congestion are such that hard measures are essential if any worthwhile and enduring improvements are to be made.

4.32. Freight vehicles and buses would merit different treatment but this should not cause any particular problems. The costs of HGV licences might reflect more accurately not only the damage they cause to the environment but also the real costs of the damage they inflict on the road system, the buildings adjacent to the roads and the services beneath them and this needs more careful evaluation.

Speed limits

4.33. Motorists generally take scant notice of speed limits but when lower limits were introduced during the 1973 energy crisis, there was widespread albeit comparatively short term compliance. The police say that they find it very difficult or virtually impossible to enforce speed limits. Greater use of modern technology and a change in the law to permit use of HGV tachometer records in evidence would help them. But adoption of lower speeds by road users requires a major reversal of the culture of speed, persistently promoted by all types of motoring interest. In the context of wide ranging restraints introduced to reduce pollution, lower speed limits would be logical.

4.34. Lower speeds would have many beneficial effects; reducing energy consumption, traffic noise and the number and severity of accidents. The most efficient use of fuel in cars is at speeds of 40 - 50mph, but it has been estimated that approximately 5% of fuel could be saved by cutting the upper speed limit to 60mph and enforcing it.

Road accidents

4.35. In any study concerned with environmental disbenefits, the problem of road traffic accidents must loom large. The Government is already moving to reduce the rate of road accidents by concentrating on three of the primary causes; behaviour, vehicle performance, and road layout. In spite of increasing traffic, the broad accident trend is downwards. However, this improvement is neither sufficient nor fast enough.

4.36. A frequently recorded causative effect in traffic accidents is excessive speed. This is speed which is excessive for the circumstances, not always high speed. For instance, a speed of 70mph on a motorway is quite acceptable in clear and uncongested conditions but extremely dangerous in fog; 30mph is usually far too fast for crowded shopping centres. High speed increases braking distance and reduces safety factors. Much has been done to improve vehicle performance and safety, although as vehicles approach the end of their lives they may require more frequent checks than the annual MOT Test. Small, low cost road improvements have shown excellent results, but there is still a great deal that could be done in this area. Road traffic accidents are predominantly a feature of the urban scene where they go hand in hand with other environmental disbenefits; streets cluttered with parked cars, rat running to avoid congested roads, urban layout and design created before the advent of the car and the conflict ridden mix of heavy vehicles, light vehicles, cyclists and pedestrians. Imprudent speed is often a cause of urban road traffic accidents and of anxiety among residents, but it is essentially a symptom of the unsuitability of the urban environment to the use to which it is subjected by road traffic.

4.37. In dealing with accidents in urban areas, many of the recommendations in the Institution's report, Congestion, will be particularly effective. Traffic calming in particular has much to offer in reducing the dominance of the car in residential areas, diminishing noise and the threat of moving vehicles to pedestrians and cyclists by minimising speed and maximising driver awareness and care. Road narrowing, road speed humps and tables, enhanced planting and other devices all have a part to play.

4.38. The Institution approves of the Government's measures to reduce urban road traffic accidents by a wide spectrum of measures, including education, training, publicity, small road improvements and better vehicle maintenance, but stresses that what is overwhelmingly required is adaptation of the urban environment, not for traffic but for people.

New roads

4.39. It is significant that Environmental Impact Assessments have rarely resulted in any major changes in the planned national road infrastructure construction programme. The appraisal processes have enabled more or less optimised schemes to be identified, striking some kind of local environmental balance. The main issue, however, must always be whether the planned road or roads are really necessary at all and in some cases there are growing doubts in this respect.

4.40. It must be borne in mind, of course, that unilateral action by the UK to limit transport infrastructure provision could have adverse effects on the nation's business and manufacturing performance, and could prejudice its export capacity. In this, as in all other national endeavours, a sensible balance must be maintained. However, in view of the forecast increases in car mileage and bearing in mind that better inter-urban roads tend to feed traffic at a faster rate into already congested urban road systems, the conventional wisdom of new road building faces a new challenge. Would it not be wiser to reduce car mileage and make better use of existing roads?

4.41. Each mile of new motorway involves a land take of around 10ha. It has been estimated that up to approximately 1,600ha of countryside are sterilised by road building each year. The visual intrusion of new main roads, no matter how carefully they are planned and constructed, is considerable. Community severance can have wide reaching and long lasting adverse effects. Better understanding of ecological impact and imbalances resulting from new transport infrastructure are causing increasing unease. The Government's current road building programme contains numerous future problems in these respects.

Environmental disbenefits

4.42. The appraisal frameworks set environmental disbenefits in the context of an economic evaluation of construction cost against user cost benefits. The selection of preferred solutions puts a heavy premium on maximising user benefits and minimising costs. Reduction in environmental disbenefits normally means increased construction costs without any apparent compensating user benefits. This is because no economic evaluation is available for such environmental factors. Nor are there formal thresholds of acceptability for environmental factors although consultation and public inquiry processes seek to establish some kind of balance.

4.43. It is important that environmental benefits are given (and are seen to be given) full weight in both the initial studies which may result in a new road or improvement and also in the detailed planning for the works. The duty of civil engineers to resist initiatives which would reduce costs by penalising the environment will be reinforced by Environmental Impact Assessments required by EC regulations.

Noise

4.44. Changes in road traffic noise flow from changes in the volume of traffic, the construction of new roads, the effects of construction and use regulations and enforcement. Volume changes due to growth, the provision of better alternative routes or traffic diversions. Traffic noise appraisals are often a part of the assessment of planning and traffic management proposals, but only in the case of new road construction is there provision for compensation when noise is predicted to exceed 68dB(A) on the L10 scale. It is not clear that this level is appropriate in all or any circumstances. Furthermore, it is not satisfactory that there is no statutory responsibility placed on highway authorities to monitor traffic noise and take action to mitigate its effects when above stated thresholds.

Pedestrians and cyclists

4.45. Pedestrians and cyclists suffer more from pollution than car owners. They are disadvantaged at almost every turn when using the road system. They receive, at short range, the gaseous emissions of vehicles, they are highly vulnerable and are subject to greater impact of noise. They are most aware of visual intrusion and community severance and are acutely vulnerable to the proximity of lorries and roadworks. Furthermore, cyclists have been especially disadvantaged by disregard in the way in which modern road systems are laid out.

Pedestrians

4.46. Pedestrians are not a minority interest. Pedestrianisation has been widely adopted, often against opposition, but there are many cases where it is has been defeated by a combination of opposition from trading and motoring interests. The surge in interest in environmental matters will give new impetus to the promoters of such schemes and the time is ripe for the widespread adoption of pedestrianisation of town centre and conservation areas combined with improved public transport and park and ride facilities.

4.47. Where full pedestrianisation is not practical, adoption of demand management should open up the potential for improved surface level crossings of traffic. Currently, there is reliance on conventional zebra and pelican crossings, but road narrowings and raised tables associated with signal controls increase the visual prominence of pedestrians and lower accident risk by enhancing driver awareness of pedestrians. The Department of Transport and the Institution of Highways and Transportation have done a good deal to promote the techniques and good practice of aiding pedestrian movement, but this work needs expansion by highway authorities.

Cyclists

4.48. Cyclists have an unhappy record in attracting the sympathies of highway authorities and the motoring public. Only in places like Cambridge and Peterborough, where the topography is favourable, or Stevenage, where the new town was laid out to provide special and widespread facilities for cyclists, does cycling flourish. Extensive promotion by the Department of Transport, the Institution of Highways and Transportation and interest groups has secured some notable cycling experiments, but no marked improvement in provision for the use of the bicycle.

4.49. Cyclists who are determined enough to commute by bicycle in cities can often claim time savings, as well as benefit to the community by not adding to congestion. Inducement to the use of a bicycle is undoubtedly hampered by the risks and discomfort. The road system is not such that it can cope with present levels of traffic, and while a substantial increase in the number of cyclists would create serious problems there is scope for wider use of cycles in the present situation.

4.50. Few highway authorities have accepted priorities for the allocation of resources for the creation of significant amounts of dedicated cycleways. Nor are many urban areas conveniently laid out for this. Modification of existing road geometry to make it less hazardous for cyclists is not really practical while cars and lorries are the principal concern, but provision on the Stevenage or Peterborough models has been a success. The growing impact of congestion is likely, in the short term, to increase the number of cyclists.

4.51. In the longer term, demand management by road pricing may create a new perception amongst urban dwellers that the bicycle is a mode of transport which offers convenience, adaptability and economy. This is a perception which the Dutch have not lost, but the Netherlands is a flat country. In the UK, the use of the bicycle is unlikely to rise to Dutch levels, but the potential is there to which highway authorities may need to respond. As urban road congestion is brought under control by road pricing, resources will be released to enhance the provision for cycling and an opportunity provided for reduction in pressure on public transport systems.

4.52. As with every other aspect of provision for transportation, it is evident that travel on foot or by bicycle can only be satisfactorily promoted and provided for by a coordinated approach to all modes of surface transport.

Conclusions

4.53. In the absence of targets and objectives which include limitations on environmental disbenefits such as noise, air pollution, vibration and visual intrusion, the opportunities for rational assessment of new road proposals, traffic management measures and other regulations are reduced. The result is a capricious and uneven planning system which incurs long delays. Steps should be taken to establish Environmental Impact Assessments on a systematic basis with coherent criteria for all types of substantial highway proposals.

4.54. The implications of growing and unlimited vehicle ownership, such as the saturation of road space, have been recognised. Vehicle mileage must be restrained to predetermined targets. The means to this end include the introduction of road pricing, increasing the real price of petrol and abolishing vehicle excise duty in favour of increased duty on petrol. Consideration should be given to reducing the upper speed limit for cars, and also to returning the HGV speed limit to 50mph.

4.55. The policy for new inter urban road building should be reviewed because it will contribute to the choking of cities where space for road building is not available, nor desirable. Land use policies should be based upon shared concepts of environmental conservation. These concepts must be accepted within the EC.

Options for action to contain pollution
Rail transport

4.56. Rail transport pollutes and creates environmental disbenefits in the following ways

(a) gaseous emissions
(b) noise and vibration
(c) congestion
(d) land take, blight, community severance, visual intrusion and ecological damage
(e) accidents.

Atmospheric pollution

4.57. Great improvements in the control of gaseous emissions of railways have been achieved coincidentally by the change from coal fired engines to diesel and electric power.

4.58. Emissions of carbon dioxide by rail transport are now relatively insignificant (see Annex 4.D), and emissions of nitrogen oxides amount to only 2% of the total for the UK. Carbon monoxide from railway sources amounts to only 0.2% of the UK total (shown in Annex 4.D). Atmospheric pollution from railways can be significantly reduced by electrification subject to the method of power generation used. Whilst the aim should be to limit these emissions even further, especially the nitrogen oxides and particulates from diesel power units, reducing emissions from diesel traction would have a minimal effect compared to the emissions from other sources such as power stations and road transport.

Noise

4.59. The absence of a statutory assessment framework for noise compensation on new rail projects results in much subjective evaluation and argument regarding any new railway operation. Noise is the main source of concern to the public in considering new railway proposals, and is the key issue in the widespread local opposition to the Channel Tunnel Rail Link (CTRL). Noise intrusion is an existing problem for people who live and work near to busy railways. For example, train noise 25m from the track side measures 92dB(A) for trains in Kent travelling at 90mph and 99dB(A) for first generation TGV trains at 168mph on the South East routes from Paris. New trains for the CTRL would be designed to produce no more than 93dB(A) at their 140mph speed measured 25m from the track side.

4.60. Generally trains pass less frequently than road vehicles but emit more noise when they do. Their intrusive qualities are partly a reflection of their intermittent nature. British Rail (BR) receive most complaints from residents adjacent to lines where diesel locomotives under heavy load are climbing a gradient or where, for example, they stand for a long time with engines idling at signals.

4.61. Railway noise is undoubtedly an environmental problem and the Institution welcomes the recent Department of Transport move to set up a committee to recommend a national noise standard for new railway lines.

4.62. What is required in respect of mitigation of noise nuisance from railways are measures to

(a) reduce the noise emitted, particularly at wheel/rail interface
(b) reduce noise transmission where necessary by the use of noise barriers (a 2m high barrier close to the track will reduce noise levels by up to 10dB), embankments, cuttings and tunnels (for existing railways using diesel traction, these remedies would only be partially effective or prohibitively expensive)
(c) adopt noise level regulations similar to those for roads under which houses become eligible for insulation grants where the noise exceeds a qualifying level.

4.63. In this latter connection noise levels reduce with increasing distance from the track. They are estimated to fall by around 20dB as the distance from the track increases from 25m to 200m. In addition, the ground will absorb some sound at certain frequencies.

4.64. Much has already been achieved by track and train designers to reduce noise. Disc braked modern trains running on well maintained continuously welded rail for instance are significantly less noisy. BR and London Underground are involved in continuing and fruitful research on the nature of noise emissions from wheel, track and bed, as also are the UIC Office for Research and Experiments. Many of the systems now under evaluation offer encouraging potential for new builds of rolling stock. Nevertheless, railways operate in an uncertain climate regarding noise emissions, with no statutory obligations. Targets should be set for noise intrusion from railways, with a requirement that operators reduce noise emissions or give grants for noise insulation.

Vibration

4.65. The prediction of railway vibration is not as straightforward as railway noise because local ground conditions have an important influence on the extent and nature of vibration. This is also true of the track bedding systems and the weight, suspension and speed of the trains. Most of the published information on the subject concerns buildings which are affected by urban rapid transit systems, particularly those underground.

4.66. Research has shown that there is a major difference between passenger and freight trains. Passenger vehicles with their lighter axle loads and complex suspension systems rarely create vibration perceptible 25m from the track side even when travelling at high speed. Freight vehicles, however, with axle loads up to 25 tonnes and simple suspension systems are the dominant cause of vibration.

4.67. Various designs of track have been tested with the object of reducing vibration and some of these have been comparatively successful. These designs are costly and could not be used for surface railways without a major injection of capital, but they might be used in sensitive positions such as the proposed London Cross Rail lines. However,

there is little need for the introduction of measures to reduce vibration as generally it is not a major problem. Railway vibration is rarely at a level which causes damage to buildings, the usual cause of public concern, but as with noise, statutory limits on what are acceptable levels of vibration are required.

Congestion

4.68. Congestion on the railways is predominantly occurring in the major cities and London in particular where it is a considerable cause of public complaint. However it is spreading to many of the InterCity and Network SouthEast services of BR outside London. The Institution's report, Congestion, made a series of recommendations based on the primary need for intelligent co-ordination of all transport systems. Basically within such a co-ordinated system the need in respect of rail systems is to increase capacity by

(a)   increasing the length of trains and platforms
(b)   hastening the provision of new rolling stock
(c)   increasing fares where necessary to discourage leisure travellers during peak hours
(d)   constructing the new lines, both BR's London Cross Rail and new Underground as identified by the Central London Rail Study
(e)   providing light rapid transit systems where practicable and environmentally acceptable
(f)   proceeding as a matter of priority with the package of additional measures recommended by the Central London Rail Study such as the works to modernise the London Underground stations.

4.69. The cost of implementing these measures would be extremely difficult for BR and London Regional Transport to meet, but the severity of congestion and its effects, particularly in London, are such that the Institution considers that Government grant funding should be provided.

Land take, blight, community severance and visual intrusion

4.70. The large areas of land required for the construction of new lines and their visual, environmental and ecological intrusion, cause widespread opposition from local residents who fear not only noise but also the community severance which may occur together with blight on large areas of land along proposed routes. The best example of the problems which arise is the proposed Channel Tunnel Rail Link, which has attracted fierce opposition on all the above counts. The examination of alternative routes has caused large areas of blight as it is difficult for owners to sell houses along any of the proposed routes. BR operates an *ex gratia* scheme to buy blighted houses but sellers have to prove that they are suffering real hardship, that they need to sell for reasons unconnected with the new line, and that their homes lie along one of the proposed routes. Each route could affect up to around 2,500 houses in London alone and with several alternative routes this is a widespread problem with severe cost implications. SNCF has less problems with new route selection because they treat the owners of blighted houses more generously. The problems faced by SNCF are of a lower order as France is over twice the size of the UK with slightly less population so that a line can be planned largely to avoid areas of population. The CTRL must pass through areas of London and the densely populated South East. In these circumstances, the Institution believes that compensation for blighted houses should be handled sympathetically and with generosity.

4.71. It would appear from experience with Docklands Light Railway and light rail lines in Manchester, South Yorkshire and West Midlands, that, unless house demolition is involved, the merits of such schemes are recognised. Also the growing acceptance of the need for

Environmental Impact Assessments and the development of EC regulations for each assessment should help to ensure reduced public opposition to future schemes.

4.72. Much can be done to ameliorate the land take, visual intrusion, environmental and ecological effects of new rail lines by careful and sympathetic planning. BR are taking the lead in measures to achieve improvements and is also, under its Director of Research at Derby and through its businesses, seeking to define and establish best practice in all its activities, balancing operational and environmental needs. This work will establish the basis for future cooperation with Local Authorities, the Railway Heritage Trust, the Nature Conservancy Council and other outside bodies.

General

4.73. In practically all respects rail transport is less of a threat to the environment in terms of passenger distance travelled than road transport. Even the problems foreseen with the construction of the CTRL must be set against the similar problems which would arise if it were not constructed and additional road provision proved necessary. For these and other reasons, the Institution believes that within a coordinated transportation system, policy should be directed to the transfer, where possible, of passengers and freight from the road system to rail, but it is recognised that this would require considerably increased grant provision for rail systems. The Government should consider investing in railways, both for new lines and improvements, using similar criteria to its investment in roads. At present the Government authorises BR to spend its own money but does not 'give' investment cash in the same way as for roads.

4.74. In free market terms subsidy is inefficient. Where, however, the alternative to subsidising the railways is increased pressure on the already congested road system, with increased costs to business and industry and greater damage to the environment, the operation of a free market strategy creates a framework for distortion.

Light rail systems

4.75. In the last few years, light rapid transit systems have gained popular support as potential environmentally attractive urban transport systems. The majority of proposals are for light rail systems with the Tyne and Wear Metro and the Docklands Light Railway operational and being extended, Greater Manchester's Metrolink under construction, and Parliamentary Powers granted for South Yorkshire, West Midlands and Avon. Some 40 other cities in the UK are currently considering light rail.

4.76. Other forms of light rapid transit systems include monorails (e.g. Alton Towers, Merryhill Shopping Centre), rubber-tyred peoplemovers (e.g. the Westinghouse Systems at Gatwick and Stansted, the Briway System proposed for Southampton), magnetic levitation systems (e.g. Birmingham International Airport).

4.77. Light rapid transit systems are all electrically powered and therefore do not create directly any atmospheric pollution. They also have very low noise levels, although careful design of track, structures and vehicles is necessary to eliminate any potential problems and good levels of maintenance are required. Vibration is similarly a minimal problem if careful attention is given to the design of any supporting structures.

4.78. Light rail systems can be integrated comparatively easily into existing urban areas, making use of available rights of way, such as former rail alignments, highway alignments or off-highway alignments.

4.79. Land take requirements are small compared to new highways or fully segregated rail systems and careful route planning can minimise blight. Light rail tracks can be crossed by vehicles and pedestrians at grade and therefore problems of community severance can be avoided. Modern technology has reduced the visual impact of the overhead power supply lines. Careful attention to detailed design can help to minimise the adverse impacts of blight, visual intrusion and landtake.

4.80. Light rail will only be feasible economically in urban areas where there are existing or potential passenger flows of at least 2,000 passengers per hour. However, experience in other European countries and in North America confirms that light rail systems could play a major role in promoting environmentally acceptable transport in British cities.

**Options for action to contain pollution
Air transport**

4.81. Air transport is growing sharply throughout the world. The Civil Aviation Authority estimates that total world scheduled air passenger traffic will rise from the present 1.1bn to 2bn by the year 2000. In the UK the numbers are expected to increase from a total of 86M in 1987 to between 164M and 234M by 2005, and the current world aircraft fleet of 6,400 is expected to rise to 14,800. At the same time, however, widespread technological advances are being introduced or are in planning. It is against this background of change that the options for action to contain pollution and environmental damage must be examined.

4.82. Air transport creates significant environmental disbenefits and pollution in the following categories:

(a) gaseous emissions (atmospheric pollution)
(b) noise
(c) congestion
(d) land take, blight, community disturbance, visual intrusion and ecological damage
(e) accidents.

Atmospheric pollution

4.83. The principal polluting gases emitted by aircraft are carbon dioxide and nitrogen oxides. The emissions are small compared to road transport and difficulties of measurement renders uncertain the figures. It has been estimated for instance that aircraft produce around 2% of airborne nitrogen oxides, and the rest come from road traffic, power stations, etc. However, aircraft emissions of this gas at cruise altitudes and high speed may be more significant but there is no dependable means of measurement. Furthermore, the technology to reduce nitrogen oxide emissions without reducing safety aspects is not available.

4.84. Modern engines are certainly cleaner than older designs and the steady phasing out of older aircraft will reduce emissions. In addition, useful improvements have been made in the reduction of unburnt hydrocarbons and smoke emissions. However, this is a highly complex subject for aircraft engine design and work on these problems is still in hand.

Noise

4.85. There is no absolute measure of disturbance from aircraft noise, and reactions from individuals differ. Airports are the source, however, directly and indirectly of the most disturbing noise problems arising from any class of transportation. The Noise and Number Index (NNI) has generally been regarded in the UK as a reasonable guide to aircraft noise, but the use of different noise measurement methods for each mode of transport confuses the public. The Department of Transport's move towards the use of Leq is therefore supported, provided that it is coupled with the continued publication and monitoring of our noise contours.

4.86. Considerable advances have been made in reducing the noise generated by individual aircraft. Compared with the first generation civil transport aircraft, for instance, (such as the Boeing 707 - 300 series) third generation aircraft are up to 85% less noisy. The Government in the UK is committed to improving noise levels and has taken action to ban the noisier aircraft from UK airports following the 1979 EC Directive on aircraft noise. As a result, noise has been significantly reduced in spite of the increasing numbers of flights. At Heathrow for instance the 35 NNI contour now covers 600,000 people, whereas in 1978 it covered 2M.

4.87. The main factors which have contributed to the reduction in aircraft noise from civil airports can be summarised as follows:

(a) Subsonic jet aircraft without a noise certificate which are UK registered were banned from UK airports from 1st January 1986.

(b) Foreign registered aircraft of the same type were banned from 1st January 1988.

(c) Advances in aircraft technology. Subsonic jet aircraft with a noise certificate have to meet the standards laid down in ICAOs 'Aircraft Noise' and fall into two categories; Chapter 2 aircraft (e.g. Boeing 727s, and earlier type 737s and 747s and Douglas DC9s) and the more stringent Chapter 3 aircraft.

(d) Differential airport charges. British Airports Authority has operated a system of noise related charges for several years.

(e) Operational control over air traffic during arrivals and departures at airports, adopting climb and descent profiles to minimise noise levels over sensitive areas. The newer aircraft, with high by-pass ratio engines create the least noise impact on departure by their rapid climb capacity without any thrust reductions for noise abatement purposes.

(f) Restrictions on airport use at certain times such as the night curfew at Heathrow.

(g) The reduction of ground noise where possible by the erection of barriers such as earth mounds, walls and fences.

4.88. Future improvements will come mainly from the eventual banning of Chapter 2 aircraft. The European Commission is now considering regulations to introduce a non-addition rule for these aircraft and subsequent measures to ban them. The airlines are disputing the latter measure fiercely because of the enormous operational costs. Chapter 2 aircraft comprise around 85% of the world's airline fleet. They have been entering service up to the present time and, with a life of 25 years or more, there is a long period of use to come for these noisy aircraft. No single European nation can easily take unilateral action to ban these aircraft because the airlines would merely use alternative airports in neighbouring countries thus commercially penalising the originator of the ban.

4.89. It is generally agreed that once the Chapter 2 aircraft are withdrawn from use, we will have achieved the last major development in aircraft noise reduction using current technology although further advances in engine design may help. On the other hand, the probable development of supersonic and hypersonic aircraft may pose a new threat.

4.90. If continued growth in air traffic movements is to be accepted, there is little further practicable action which can be taken other than the measures outlined above to reduce airport and aircraft noise unless restrictions are imposed on the number of flights allowed, although the development of aircraft hush kits offers some possibility of improvement. It has been proposed that Chapter 2 aircraft should be made to use airports away from London which are less environmentally sensitive. There are telling arguments against this proposal such as

(a) the possible loss of traffic to London airports which could jeopardise its position as the major European hub
(b) the hostility of foreign operators who depend upon the use of Chapter 2 aircraft
(c) the hostility of the residents near the airports selected to receive noisy aircraft.

There is the unattractive alternative of limiting growth in all types of air traffic movements. This course of action runs counter to current expectations, but noise and other forms of pollution from aircraft being no different in principle from other transport related pollution, there is no logical reason why target ceilings should not be placed on aircraft noise lower than experienced now.

Congestion

4.91. The large increase in demand for international air transport has confounded most of the forecasts and the airport and air traffic control authorities have failed to meet the demand at most of the major international airports. In the UK, this has resulted in congestion in the London system in terminal, runway, airspace and ground access operations. If the forecasts given in paragraph 4.81 above are accepted, there is an urgent need to plan adequately for these increases now. In the past the response to growth problems has been *ad hoc* development on a reactive basis. What is now urgently required is a coherent strategic plan dealing with airport capacity, air space and access.

4.92. At present, British Airports Authority (BAA) is responsible for the planning and construction of Heathrow, Gatwick and Stansted airports. They state that their proposals for terminals (including a fifth terminal at Heathrow) together with the construction of a new runway in the London system after 2005, will suffice to meet the foreseeable demand into the early part of the next century. The Institution, however, believes that allowing for the completion of the planned terminal capacity taking into account

(a) the possible increase in use of larger jet aircraft and also the probable effects of airline deregulation in Europe,
(b) the further development of Luton, London Docklands and Stansted airports (the latter to a maximum of 25M passengers per annum), and
(c) the ground access problems

the total operational capacity of the London airports system will be insufficient by the turn of the century to meet the forecasts of passenger numbers.

4.93. It must also be borne in mind that air traffic increases are unlikely to cease in 2005. In view of this and because of the length of time required to construct major new infrastructure, the Institution considers that the whole subject of capacity should now be reviewed to determine the probable requirement over a longer time scale, as it may well prove necessary even to provide a new airport for the future. If this proves to be the case, early planning could go far to reduce the environmental impact of such a provision.

4.94. Much is now being done to improve the air space congestion around the UK. The new computer will soon come on line at the London Air Traffic Control Centre, which will allow the introduction of the first phase of the Central Control Function at the end of 1990. When fully operational the latter should increase the flight handling capacity of the London system at least by 30%. By around 1996 a new En Route Central Control Centre should boost en route capacity by a further 40%. Integration of European ATC systems is proceeding and the reduction of the 30 or even 50 mile separation distances which are required in some parts of Europe to the UK's standard of 5 miles will bring big capacity increases throughout the European system. However, there are some elements of mismatch between the possible traffic levels over the next decade and the timing of the ATC improvements as to create doubts about both the short and long term adequacies of the systems.

4.95. The surface access systems for the major UK airports have failed to keep pace with the traffic increases and this has resulted in severe congestion on the road accesses to Heathrow and increasing problems with traffic from the airports feeding into adjacent urban areas. New railway lines are planned to serve Heathrow, Manchester and Stansted which will certainly help to ease road congestion but will themselves create environmental problems. There are already doubts about the eventual capacity of the Stansted link (especially as it runs into the Liverpool Street terminus) and the Heathrow link which has no extension to the west and will be insufficient to meet the eventual demand.

4.96. The Institution believes that air transport growth is likely to be such that the projected increases in airport, air space and ground access capacities in the London system will be inadequate by the turn of the century and that it is essential now to plan to meet the realistic demand with a coherent strategic plan, which can be developed for the longer term.

Land take, visual intrusion and ecological damage

4.97. The land take required, on and off site, for the construction or extension of an airport have substantial and far reaching effects. A modern airport absorbs a very large land area. The sterilisation of a considerable part of this land under runways, taxiways, hardstandings, buildings and roads has a traumatic effect on the local ecology. In addition, airports create a substantial demand for supporting urban developments, for housing and associated services, air transport support services and commercial and industrial undertakings wishing to locate near an airport. The demand for land and the consequential impacts can spread for many miles around the airport. Mitigation of noise impact, for example, requires that housing be located in areas of lower NNI values. Transport links are also required, which will take up further areas of taken by road and rail construction outside the airport boundaries. Hence, the final land take and the geographical extent of ecological damage considerably exceeds the area required for the airport itself.

4.98. Visual intrusion is also a problem with the impact of numerous airport buildings and aerial arrays into previously unspoilt country areas. Loss of visual amenity, that is the loss of open countryside, off airport follows the developments referred to above. However much is done with sympathetic planning, design and landscaping to mitigate visual intrusion, the loss of countryside is a serious concern in so small an island as Britain. It is, therefore, most important that the Environmental Impact Assessments for airport developments quite clearly show the balance locally and nationally.

Conclusion

4.99. Increase in demand for international air transport has exceeded current forecasts. The Institution believes that air transport growth by the turn of the century will outstrip facilities now planned. There is an acute conflict between, on the one hand, demand for increased airport space and more intensive use of air space and, on the other, limiting air pollution, noise emissions, and housing and other infrastructure provision. There is a clear need for a realisitic assessment of need and environmental impacts, in the context of quantified national environmental targets and objectives, followed by a coherent plan for UK air transport.

ANNEX 4.A. Forecast growth in road traffic

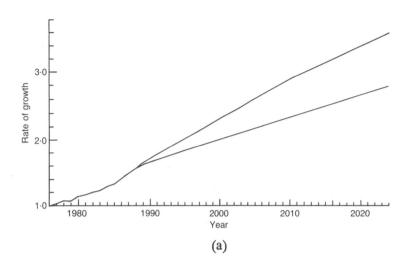

(a)

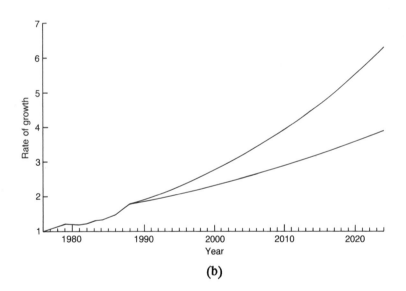

(b)

Fig. 4.1. High and low forecasts of growth in road traffic:
(a) cars; (b) HGVs over 25 t with 4 or more axles.
Source: National Road Traffic Forecasts, COBA 9 Manual May 1989

nb: Forecast years are 1989 to 2024. The figures for the years 1977 to 1988 reflect actual traffic growth from the 1976 base.

ANNEX 4.B. The extent of pollution by transport

Atmospheric pollution - carbon dioxide, hydrocarbons and nitrogen oxides

4.A.1. The contributions of transport to atmospheric pollution are almost exclusively associated with vehicle exhaust emissions, although there are minor contributions arising from the construction of transport infrastructure, such as those arising from cement production or quarrying activities. The data is incomplete and there is a need for regular update by all countries thus providing a basis for global evaluation.

4.A.2. The UK Atomic Energy Authority has estimated that the worldwide make up of the 'greenhouse effect' consists of 40% carbon dioxide from energy consumption; 15% carbon dioxide from deforestation, 20% hydrocarbons, 20% chlorofluorocarbons and 5% nitrous oxide. Of these, the significant gases emitted by transport are carbon dioxide, hydrocarbons and nitrous oxide.

4.A.3. To put these figures into perspective, it is necessary to consider the proportion attributable to transport, and the contribution of the UK against the total of world production of these gases.

4.A.4. The most recent quantifications of total world emissions are for 1980/82 and are given in Table 4.1. Of these totals the UK is responsible for 3% of carbon dioxide; 4% of hydrocarbons; and 3% of nitrogen oxides.

Table 4.1. Greenhouse gases: total emissions 1980/82

| | Million tonnes (%) | | |
	Carbon dioxide	Hydro-carbons	Nitrogen oxides
Data year	1982	1980	1980
World	4752*	57	69
EC	n/a	10.5	11.2
(EC/World)	n/a	18%	16%
UK	141*	2.24	2.26
(UK/World)	3%	4%	3%
(UK/EC)	n/a	21%	20%

* Measured as carbon.
Source: 6th Report House of Lords & UNEP Environmental Data Report.

4.A.5 Estimates of the proportions of these figures attributable to transport emissions vary. Table 4.2. shows that in the UK transport accounts for approximately

(a)   19% of carbon dioxide - third in total after power stations and industry
(b)   30% of hydrocarbons - second in total after industry
(c)   50% of nitrogen oxides - second in total after power stations.

4.A.6. As shown in Table 4.2., road vehicles are the dominant transport source of these emissions which vary with the volume of traffic and engine speed. For instance, peak emissions of nitrogen oxides are made at high speeds whereas peak emissions of carbon monoxide occur at idling speed. The greatest threat to residents, pedestrians, cyclists and indeed to occupants of the vehicles, from inhaling these gases is caused by congestion especially in urban areas, where large numbers of vehicles are standing with engines running or moving very slowly. In January 1989 the Department of the Environment monitor at Vauxhall recorded a maximum carbon monoxide level of 8.12 mg/m^3 whilst at the same time the London Scientific Services roadside monitor at County Hall recorded an average reading of 12.9 mg/m^3 over an eight hour period on one weekday and 12.4 mg/m^3 the following day. The World Health Organisations' guideline is 10 mg/m^3.

Table 4.2. Greenhouse gases: UK transport's emissions by mode 1988

| | Transport % UK/total | Thousand tonnes (% of transport) | | | |
		Road	Rail	Air	Shipping
CO_2*	19%	27,909	607	599	957
(%)		(93%)	(2%)	(2%)	(3%)
HC+	30%	545	9	-	8
(%)		(97%)	(2%)	-	(1%)
NO_x	50%	1,108	35	9	7
(%)		(95%)	(3%)	(1%)	(1%)

* Measured as carbon.
+ Non methane VOC.
- Negligible.
Source: DoE, Digest of Environmental Protection and Water Statistics No. 12 1989.

4.A.7. The Washington based Worldwatch Institute, in a report published in January 1990, estimated that more than one-fifth of the world's population now regularly breathes polluted air that fails to meet WHO standards. Air pollution which was formerly experienced only in industrial cities is now considered to be a worldwide problem.

The acid rain gases

4.A.8. Acid rain is caused mainly by emissions of sulphur oxides and nitrogen oxides. The UK is a major emitter of sulphur oxide being the worst of the OECD countries apart from the USA (see Annex 4.C). However, whilst the UK's sulphur oxide emissions in 1980 amounted to 4.8M tonnes, the contribution by transport was only 80,000 tonnes or 1.65%. Hence if sulphur oxide emissions are to be significantly reduced the focus for reduction will lie outside the transport sector.

4.A.9. The situation is different with nitrogen oxides. The total UK emission amounted to 2.3M tonnes in 1980 of which the contribution by transportation amounted to around 37%. This had increased to over 42% by 1986 (see Annex 4.E). Road transport is the principal transport source of nitrogen oxides, with HGVs and coaches accounting for nearly 50%.

4.A.10. Of the emissions referred to above, only carbon dioxide can be described as non-toxic. All the others are toxic to human, animal and plant life. There are two other major pollutants which are especially associated with petrol engined vehicles, i.e. carbon monoxide and lead. There is also one pollutant associated mainly with diesel engined vehicles i.e. particulate emission.

4.A.11. Carbon monoxide is one of the gases which is stated to contribute to the 'greenhouse effect' but it causes more concern because of its dangerous toxicity. Annex 4.D shows that of the UK 1980 total of carbon monoxide emissions amounting to 5M tonnes, 82.8% came from transport. By 1986 transport accounted for 85% of the UK total. Petrol engined vehicles are responsible for almost all of this.

4.A.12. Lead is probably the most emotive of transport's emissions in view of its well publicised effects on humans, particularly children. Annex 4.E shows that road vehicles produced 7,500 tonnes in 1980 declining to 6,500 tonnes in 1985 and then abruptly to 2,900 tonnes in 1986. There is no explanation for the massive drop shown for 1986 and this reflects doubt about the accuracy of this figure, especially as it is not reflected in the estimates of lead intake by adults in Table 4.3. The increased use of unleaded petrol will be responsible for a proportion of the decline in lead emissions.

4.A.13. Particulate emission is the main problem with diesel engined vehicles. Diesel engines are generally considered to be less harmful than petrol engines but there are suspicions that the soot particles from diesel exhausts may possibly be a cause of cancer even though this risk is considered to be slight. They are the cause of the unpleasant visible exhaust emissions associated with many HGVs.

The toxic gases

Table 4.3. UK lad intake by adults - median values micrograms of lead per kilogram of body weight per day

Year	Lead intake per day
1980	1.32
1981	1.06
1982	1.08
1983	0.96
1984	0.91
1985	0.94
1986	0.95

Source: WHO 1986 Summary of 1980-1983 Monitoring Data WHO/EHE/FOS/86.2) and WHO 1988 Summary of 1984-1985 Monitoring Data (WHO/EHE/FOS/88.4).

ANNEX 4.C.

Total emissions of traditional air pollutants, 1980 (thousand tonnes)

Country	Population (thousands)	SO_x	Partic- ulates	NO_x	CO	HC
USA	243,915	23,900	8,500	20,300	76,100	23,000
Japan	122,090	1,259	133	1,340	-	-
Germany	61,199	3,187	696	2,935	11,708	2,490
United Kingdom	56,930	4,836	290	2,264	4,999	2,241
Italy	56,664	3,211	386	1,585	5,487	1,566
France	55,630	3,512	483	1,861	6,620	1,972
Turkey	52,893	714	138	380	3,707	201
Spain	38,832	2,543	1,521	937	3,780	843
Canada	25,625	4,650	1,907	1,942	9,928	2,100
Yugoslavia	23,410	1,175	-	-	-	-
Australia	16,264	1,479	271	915	3,704	423
Netherlands	14,665	462	162	553	1,450	493
Greece	9,994	546	40	217	695	130
Belgium	9,834	856	267	317	839	339
Portugal	9,744	266	119	166	533	159
Sweden	8,398	502	170	318	1,250	410
Austria	7,586	325	50	201	1,126	251
Switzerland	6,619	126	28	196	711	311
Denmark	5,127	452	47	245	577	197
Finland	4,932	584	97	284	660	163
Norway	4,187	150	28	203	608	159
Ireland	3,543	217	94	71	497	62
New Zealand	3,309	88	21	89	566	38
Luxembourg	372	24	-	23	-	11
OECD Europe	407,395	22,500	4,600	12,800	45,200	12,000
EC	322,534	20,100	4,100	11,200	37,200	10,500
North America	269,540	28,550	10,407	22,242	86,028	25,100
Australasia	19,573	1,567	292	1,004	4,270	461
OECD total	818,598	54,000	15,500	37,500	14,100	38,500
World total	**5,024,000**	**110,000**	**59,000**	**69,000**	**193,000**	**57,000**

Source: OECD Environmental Data 1989.

ANNEX 4.D.

Pollutants: trends in emissions from road vehicles, railways and other sources[1]

(a) Nitrogen oxides[2] (thousand tonnes)   (b) Carbon monoxide (thousand tonnes)

	1978	1982	1987	% of total 1987	1978	1982	1987	% of total 1987
Domestic	66	67	74	3	599	493	421	8
Commercial/ public service[3]	62	61	61	3	13	12	10	--
Power stations	813	773	809	35	55	48	49	1
Refineries	50	42	43	2	4	4	4	--
Agriculture (fuel use)	7	5	4	--	1	1	1	--
Other industry[4]	327	244	236	10	100	74	77	1
Rail transport	43	35	35	2	17	14	13	--
Road transport	886	993	1,031	45	3,919	4,266	4,470	85
Incineration and agricultural burning	12	12	12	1	220	220	220	4
All sources (ground based)[5]	2268	2173	2303	100	4928	5131	5264	100

(c) Carbon dioxide (million tonnes)   (d) Hydro-carbons (thousand tonnes)

	1978	1982	1987	% of total 1987	1978	1982	1987	% of total 1987
Domestic	85	82	87	14	95	75	65	3
Commercial/ public service[3]	34	33	32	5	1	1	1	--
Power stations	241	224	233	37	13	13	13	1
Refineries	25	21	21	3	1	1	1	--
Agriculture (fuel use)	4	3	3	1	--	--	--	--
Other industry[4]	166	126	125	20				
(fuel use)	--	--	--	--	4	3	3	--
Rail transport	3	2	2	--	11	9	9	--
Road transport[6]	77	80	98	16	593	631	664	28
Incineration and agricultural burning	6	6	6	1	38	38	38	2
Gas production	1	4	8	1	--	--	--	--
Cement	8	7	7	1	--	--	--	--
Gas flaring	9	8	5	1	--	--	--	--
Gas leakage[7]	--	--	--	--	307	350	408	17
Industrial processes and solvent evaporation[8]	--	--	--	--	1051	1056	1072	46
Forests[9]	--	--	--	--	80	80	80	3
All sources (ground based)[5]	659	596	627	100	2196	2258	2355	100

1   Most of the figures in this table are based on constant emission factors.
2   Expressed as nitrogen dioxide equivalent.
3   Includes Miscellaneous fuel consumers.
4   Excludes power stations, refineries and agriculture.
5   Excludes emissions from fuel used for water and air transport.
6   Includes evaporative emissions from the petrol tank and carburettor of petrol-engined vehicles (Hydrocarbons table only).
7   Gas leakage is an estimate of losses during transmissions along the distribution system. The estimates have been revised after discussions with British Gas.
8   Including evaporation of motor spirit during production, storage and distribution.
9   An order of magnitude estimate of natural emissions from forests.
Source: Digest of Environmental Protection and Water Statistics No. 11, 1988 Department of the Environment.

POLLUTION

Trends in emissions from fuel combustion, UK (thousand tonnes)

Data year	Carbon monoxide	Hydro carbons[1]	Nitrogen[2] oxides	Sulphur dioxide	Carbon dioxide	Lead[3]
1980	4,085	613	905	42	80	7.5
1981	3,942	593	887	53	77	6.7
1982	4,266	631	933	49	80	6.8
1983	3,895	584	860	42	82	6.9
1984	3,884	590	888	43	86	7.2
1985	4,007	603	915	45	88	6.5
1986	4,220	630	960	50	93	2.9
1987	4,470	664	1,031	46	98	3.0

1 Includes evaporative emissions from the petrol tank and carburettor of petrol-engined vehicles.
2 Expressed as nitrogen dioxide equivalent.
3 These figures are based on average lead contents for petrol published by the Institute of Petroleum. It has been assumed that only 70% of this lead in petrol is emitted from vehicle exhausts, the remainder being retained in lubricating oil and exhaust systems.
(nb: Figures for carbon monoxide, hydrocarbons, nitrogen oxides, sulphur dioxide and carbon dioxide are based on emissions factors supplied by Warren Spring Laboratory, Department of Trade and Industry.)
Source: Digest of Environmental Protection and Water Statistics No. 11, 1988 Department of the Environment.

ANNEX 4.E.

Average noise levels: by main source of noise and by characteristics of nearest road and surrounding area (Adjusted dB(A) and scores)

	L_{Aeq}	Noise score
Main source of noise		
Traffic	55	2.3
Railway	(54)	(2.1)
Industry	(53)	(2.1)
People, children	52	2.0
Aircraft	(52)	(1.6)
Mowers	(52)	(2.1)
Construction	(50)	(2.3)
Wind or leaves	(50)	(1.6)
Animals	(48)	(1.8)
Other sources	(48)	(1.6)
Birds	(46)	(1.5)
Characteristics of nearest road		
Traffic flow:		
Free flowing	58	2.6
Interrupted	58	2.5
Little or no traffic	50	1.9
Road type:		
Motorway	(54)	(3.4)
A-road	61	2.8
B-road	55	2.3
Unclassified	52	2.0
Speed restrictions:		
30 mph	53	2.1
40 mph	57	2.5
50 mph	(59)	(2.4)
60 mph or over	(53)	(2.4)
Dual carriageway	(57)	(2.7)
Not dual carriageway	53	2.1
Bus route	58	2.5
Not bus route	52	2.0
Cul-de-sac	50	1.9
Not cul-de-sac	55	2.3
Distance (metres)		
0-2	59	2.4
3-5	55	2.2
6-10	52	2.1
11-20	52	2.1
21-50	53	2.1
51-100	(51)	(2.1)
101-200	(50)	(2.0)
Over 200	(51)	(1.8)

	L_{Aeq}	Noise score
Characteristics of nearest road (cont.)		
5-minute count of heavy vehicles		
0	51	1.9
1	55	2.3
2	(58)	(2.4)
3-5	58	2.5
6-10	(61)	(2.8)
11-20	(60)	(2.8)
Over 20	(58)	(2.8)
Characteristics of surrounding area		
Road types in area[1]		
Motorway	56	2.5
No motorways	53	2.1
A-road	55	2.3
No A-roads	52	2.0
B-road	54	2.2
No B-roads	53	2.1
Unclassified road	53	2.1
No unclassified roads	55	2.3
Distant noise sources:[2]		
Industry	55	2.2
No industry	53	2.2
Construction	(56)	(2.2)
No construction	53	2.2
Airport	54	2.2
No airport	53	2.2
Motorway	54	2.2
No motorway	54	2.2
Type of property in area[1]		
Open	50	1.9
Residential/open	52	2.1
Residential	54	2.2
All other	58	2.5

[1] A 1km square centred on the point of measurement.
[2] Outside the 1km square.

Source: DoE

ANNEX 4_G.

Passenger casualty rates by mode (the risk a traveller runs of being injured, per kilometre travelled).

	1977	1982	1987	Average 1977-1987
Air[1]				
Deaths				0.3
Seriously injured				--
Total casualties				0.4
Rail[2]				
Deaths	0.8	0.6	1.0	0.9
Seriously injured	59.7	63.6	76.3	70.0
Total casualties	60.5	64.2	77.3	70.9
Road[3]				
Bus or Coach				
Deaths	1.3	0.8	0.4	0.8
Seriously injured	25.0	23.0	20.0	22.0
Total casualties	243	243	222	238
Car				
Deaths	6.9	6.0	4.4	5.5
Seriously injured	92.0	77.0	54.0	72.0
Total casualties	431.0	366.0	320.0	361.0
Two-wheeled motor vehicles				
Deaths	177.0	109.0	100.0	125.0
Seriously injured	3,035.0	2,162.0	1,818.0	2,360.0
Total casualties	10,706.0	7,199.0	6,320.0	7,913.0
Pedal Cycles				
Deaths	59.0	46.0	49.0	54.0
Seriously injured	924.0	885.0	845.0	932.0
Total casualties	4,590.0	4,390.0	4,563.0	4,660.0
Sea[4]				
Deaths	3.4	2.1	81.4[5]	8.9
Seriously injured	--	--	39.1	17.8[6]
Total casualties	--	--	120.5	25.6[6]

1   World passenger carrying services of UK airlines for fixed wing craft over 2300kg. Passenger kilometres relate to revenue passengers only.
2   Injuries to passengers involved in railway movement accidents. The rail casualty rates have been revised since Transport Statistics Great Britain 1977-1987 to include not only people travelling in trains, but also those otherwise killed or injured by rolling stock. Railway staff are excluded.
3   Drivers and passengers in Great Britain.
4   World passenger carrying services of UK registered vessels. Passenger kilometres relate to international journeys only.
5   1987 figures include casualties resulting from the capsize of the 'Herald of Free Enterprise'
6   Average for 1983 to 1987 only

Source: Transport Statistics Great Britain 1978-1988

5. Water and public health

The water cycle
A capricious climate,
and other considerations

5.1.   The water cycle offers the appearance of an apparently ever-renewable asset both as a life-support system and as a means to economic and social progress. Fuelled by natural energy processes the prospects of the source material ever becoming depleted appear attractively remote.

5.2.   The water cycle is depicted in Figure 5.1. which shows the resource volume, located in the world's oceans and lakes, from which water is constantly being evaporated and carried over the earth's surface. Precipitation occurs and initiates the return phase of the cycle. Falling on the earth's surface the precipitated water then commences its journey back to the overall resource volume from whence it came.

5.3.   Exploiting the cycle is no easy process, not least because of the cycle's inherently capricious behaviour. That capriciousness is seen in the extremes of drought and flood - and is reinforced by the inevitability that, being a cycle, actions arising in one phase are likely to have repercussions in others.

5.4.   In the process of its journey, as the diagram depicts, some water will make its way by river systems (and some will be evaporated before it reaches the sea), some will enter underground strata and continue its journey as groundwater. Some will be taken and used for public supply, some for industry, and some for agriculture. Such uses however are largely diversions during which the quality of the water concerned deteriorates before it rejoins the return phase of the cycle.

5.5.   The technology for the use of this particular great source of power in nature has been developed by the engineer. In so doing he has to bear in mind not only the physically attainable, but also the economically viable and the environmentally desirable, and he has to accept a balance between all three. However, in the process of reaching that balance, it is ultimately the depth of the client's pocket, and his reactions to the environment, which largely determine how the

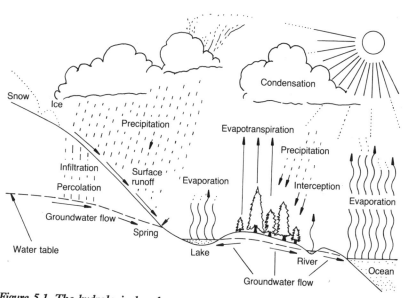

Figure 5.1. The hydrological cycle.
Reproduced with permission of Longman Group (Phillips/Turton "Environment, Man & Economic Change"

53

engineer's completed works actually affect the water cycle. Within the public water service, it is the customer who ultimately pays the environmental costs.

Groundwater

5.6.   Geology determines whether, within the water cycle's return phase, the movement of returning water is above or below the earth's surface. Groundwater is the name given to water either passing through or retained within underground strata.   Under natural conditions groundwater emerges again in due course as springs supporting river and stream flows.   Spring flow may, in fact, arise beneath the sea's surface, the return to source then being accomplished directly.

5.7.   Water's solvent properties cause minerals, from the strata through which it passes, to be taken into solution.   Groundwaters and surface water thus differ in chemical composition.   The strata may, additionally, also provide a purifying effect as groundwater passes through them. Groundwater which is chemically suitable for public use often requires little by way of treatment to render it potable.   By contrast the chemical content of some groundwaters is such that treatment, even where practicable, would not be economic.

5.8.   Were groundwater not taken, the level at which it stands within the strata (the water table) would be influenced only by incoming percolation and outgoing spring flow.   However, where abstractions are made, the periodic fluctuations of the water table are influenced by that situation and also by little of such water being returned after use to the strata from which it came.

5.9.   Pollution entering surface waters becomes diluted, and can be ameliorated by reactions taking place in those waters.   It is, however, also carried away relatively rapidly from the location at which entry took place.   With groundwaters removal from the scene is likely to be protracted and a contaminated aquifer remains contaminated for a much longer time than surface water.

Abstraction and discharge

5.10. Reference was made in paragraph 5.4 to the way in which abstractions are made from the return phase of the water cycle.   An abstraction - which might well be supported by storage in one form or another - usually leads to the used water being discharged again back into the cycle.   Such discharges are usually made within the same river basin, but may occasionally be into an entirely different catchment. Some are made to underground strata whilst others go directly to estuaries or the sea, as is reflected in recent Government responses to the phasing out of such discharges.

Entity of the Environment

5.11. The above references to the water cycle emphasise its integral nature, and its importance both as a habitat and a life support system for a wide variety of flora and fauna.   That situation, however, should not be permitted to obscure the perspective of the water cycle's place within a larger whole, the natural environment.

5.12. Just as there are interactions between phases of the water cycle so are there knock-on and cost-creating effects on the water cycle by other aspects of the environment.   Most of these reflect the presence of man - aerial emissions falling back to earth, postulated climatic change, energy use, transport and disposal of polluting substances.

Administrative and enabling systems
Overall situation

5.13. The growth of organisations for supplying water, and for taking it away again as sewage is the basis of the history of the water industry. This has been paralleled by the development of legislation directed to regulating their activities relative to the water cycle.

•5.14. The events calling for such regulation follow a pattern

(a)   exploitation and over-exploitation of the resource - leading to decline and deterioration, sometimes lasting for several decades, and adverse environmental effects

(b)   the need to apply both technology and legislation to contain that situation

(c)   recovery, through such application, often with an associated financial commitment.

5.15. Before looking more closely at some of the adverse effects which may arise within the water cycle, this section draws attention to the contemporary administrative systems and the associated 'doing' and 'regulating' organisations. This is necessarily an abbreviated overview in which it should be noted that differing administrative arrangements apply in England and Wales, in Scotland, and in Northern Ireland. The legislation differs, sometimes in detailed form sometimes in its actual existence, across the UK and reflects variations in both physical and political situations in national groupings and this in turn shapes the detail of the administrative arrangements.

Abstractions made from water sources

5.16. From the mid 1960s most abstraction (i.e. boreholes and wells, reservoirs and directly from streams) in England and Wales became subject to licensing. Many of the early licences, however, simply regularised abstractions at the time licensing was introduced. Subsequently water resource relationships have become better understood, and more flexible methods of source utilisation have been introduced. The National Rivers Authority is the responsible body in England and Wales. For abstractions for public supplies Government plays the supervisory role in Scotland; in Northern Ireland water matters generally are overseen by Government.

Water supply

5.17. Water supply legislation has sought to ensure that good contemporary practice should apply throughout the UK, and that piped supplies, public and private, should be wholesome. In recent years EC legislation has contributed measures specified as requisite to the quality of potable water. Many of those measures are now mandatory.

5.18. In England and Wales public supplies are the responsibility of the ten recently created water service plcs, together with the companies supplying water only, which have their origins in the nineteenth century. In Scotland the system is under public control, and in Northern Ireland is a function of Government.

Discharges of polluted water

5.19. Discharges (i.e. effluents, leachates, spillages) contain not only human wastes of sewerage systems, but the residual products of domestic, industrial and agricultural activities. Legislation has sought to control the quantity and nature of the polluting substances present in a discharge to which consent has been given; penalised infringements of the specific content of such a consent; and outlawed those discharges to which consent has not been given.

5.20. The National Rivers Authority acts as gamekeeper in England and Wales. In Scotland the machinery for giving consent, where not under direct local authority control, operates under local authority influence. In Northern Ireland water functions are under Government control.

Sewerage and sewage disposal

5.21. Concern about public health was the impetus behind the engineering of both piped water supplies and sewerage infrastructure.

The Victorian civil engineer faced an enormous public health challenge. Movement to an urban waterborne sewerage system became widespread. The problem of waterborne disease was tackled by the design and construction of water purification plants and sewage conveyance and treatment works. The civil engineer's contribution to preventing health problems was at that time greater than the medical profession's ability to cure waterborne diseases, once it had occurred. The importance of the link between public health practised by the civil engineering profession and medical health practised by the medical profession cannot be overemphasised. Such links can only be encouraged within an appropriate legal framework.

5.22. The last quarter of the nineteenth century then saw progress in defining the quality required for discharges of sewage. Not until 1915 did specific requirements became attached to official advice and the Royal Commission standard was introduced. Subsequently greater understanding and successive legislation have enabled discharges of treated sewage to be approved in a more flexible way, not possible with 'blanket' standards.

5.23. Other operators are industrial organisations and private estates. In Scotland public sewerage and sewage treatment is a local authority function, with 'private' operators also as in England and Wales. In Northern Ireland the public systems are the responsibility of the Government.

Land drainage and flood protection

5.24. The protection of low lying land from inundation, and the drainage of agricultural land is a long standing engineering activity. Currently, in England and Wales, the National Rivers Authority is responsible for what the Water Act 1989 refers to as 'flood defence', a change in emphasis after almost 60 years of successive piecemeal legislation directed at land drainage.

5.25. The situation is complicated by

(a) the presence of other bodies (i.e. internal drainage boards, and local authorities) with defined powers to act in this area. Another department of Government (the MAFF) is primarily responsible, DoE being involved with other water cycle matters.
(b) responsibility distinctions between protecting low-lying coastal land from inundation by either salt or fresh water and protecting the coastline itself from erosion.

5.26. In Scotland urban flood protection, including that from seawater flooding, falls within the local government machinery. The improvement of agricultural land by drainage works is administered by Government. In Northern Ireland the Ministry of Agriculture is responsible for land drainage and sea defence, expenditure being permissible only on designated watercourses.

Summary - river basin management

5.27. With many bodies and organisations responsible for water cycle activities it becomes increasingly desirable that there should be means not only to regulate, but to coordinate comprehensively within river basins. To a degree machinery now exists in England and Wales in the National Rivers Authority. That body issues licences for water abstractions and consents for effluent discharges; it monitors their effects, and has powers to enforce compliance through the courts.

5.28. Not all water cycle matters, however, fall under the same department of Government. Additionally, such activities as waste disposal, the responsibility of both central and local government, can affect management of water resources if liaison and consultation is ineffective.

5.29. In its Second Report on Toxic Waste (February 1989) the House of Commons Environment committee sought the creation of a national regulatory body - the Environmental Protection Agency. A proposal not favoured by Government at the time. Nevertheless, the Institution supports the view that the way forward, not only for the water cycle but for the natural environment as a whole, lies in the creation of such a body. That could not be achieved over night, but the existence of the NRA in England and Wales provides an opportunity to consider a water cycle protection agency as an initial step.

Water quality standards

5.30. Water is a primary vector for the transmission of constituents potentially hazardous to health. Chemical and biological constituents are the most significant including nitrates; nitrite from agricultural land; lead, copper and aluminium from the delivery system; viruses and parasites including *Giardia lamblia* and *Cryptosporidium* from sources polluted by competing water uses. The presence of lead piping is usually an historical legacy, but when the water supply is acidic, lead finds its way into solution, with possible long term detrimental accumulation in humans. Medical research is not united on the risk of lead accumulation in human tissue, but research indicates that it can affect brain development, and or cause hyperactivity. No detailed standards are agreed but WHO drinking water standards give allowable lead concentration of 0.05mg/litre.

5.31. The operations of the EC have, from the mid-1970s, led to a series of directives, largely (as far as the water environment is concerned) introducing quality standards applicable to specific uses and activities.

5.32. Of more immediate relevance are those for

(a)   water for human consumption (80/778/EEC)
(b)   surface water abstracted for drinking water (75/440/EEC)
(c)   protection of groundwater from pollution (80/68/EEC)
(d)   discharge of dangerous substances (76/464/EEC)
(e)   bathing water (76/160/EEC)
(f)   use of sewage sludge in agriculture (86/278/EEC)
(g)   environmental assessment of certain projects (85/337/EEC)

5.33. Expert opinion about the relevance of some of the values ascribed to individual measures varies - but EC law calls for their observance. The technology for the purpose is available, but time and cost are currently constraints in complying.

5.34. Surveys of British drinking water supplies indicates that a significant number of treated water supplies fall below EC standards. The scale of the problem is considerable due to the range of hazardous constituents, which in turn is further exacerbated by the risk of pollution of source water supplies by accidental spillage or fallout. Treatment of water supplies is only one part of the safe management of water supplies. The management of the river or groundwater basin or the source areas of the water supply is another essential part. Multiple use of water supplies is often in conflict, e.g. a major source of *Cryptosporidium* is animal excrement washed off the land. Greater understanding, planning and management is required to maintain a safe drinking water supply for the majority of the British population, measuring up to EC standards.

5.35. It is inescapable that the improvement of environmental conditions, and their subsequent maintenance, will introduce costs which have to be met. Such costs will exceed those applicable whilst deterioration was taking place - and it may well be that the charges will fall in different quarters.

5.36. The Institution supports the basic principle of the polluter pays, but if conditions of commercial competition were to be removed from the equation, the costs would be transferred to customers purchasing from the 'polluter' concerned. In an environmental situation matters are unlikely to be so clear-cut and communities must themselves be prepared to meet at least some part of the cost of securing the environmental quality they want.

Pollution of inland waters
Surface waters

5.37. The Environmental Protection Bill defines pollution as 'the release into any environmental medium . . . of substances . . . capable of causing harm to man or any other living organisms supported by the environment'. The vulnerability of surface waters to the entry of that kind of pollution during the 'return' phase of the water cycle has already been emphasised.

5.38. There is often some degree to which the environment can assimilate polluting substances - their potential to cause harm is then a dominant factor only if that natural capability becomes overloaded. Consent to the discharge of effluents into the water cycle contain specific terms which have the object of avoiding environmental overloading. Not all discharges have been approved; and those which have may fail to comply with the detail contained within the consent conditions.

5.39. Overloading discharges can arise from such situations as

(a) ineffective treatment, even where treatment is effective however such discharges can be affected by accident, error, or unauthorised action within the catchment of the system draining to the discharge point
(b) the operation of storm and emergency overflows within sewerage systems after heavy rain, or for physical and mechanical reasons
(c) contemporary agricultural practices - producing either diffuse discharges from the run-off from agricultural land, or more localised effects arising from animal wastes and silage
(d) leachates arising within wastes disposal sites
(e) 'natural' effects, such as the growth of toxic algae, or the flushing of acidic matter from moorland catchments after dry weather
(f) 'accidental' occurrences, such as transport accidents: the leakage, overfilling, or vandalism of tanks containing polluting substances.
(g) human error, failure to comply with stipulated procedures or to appreciate cause-and-effect situations
(i) unauthorised discharges such as illegal waste disposal.

5.40. As far as discharges of treated sewage in England and Wales are concerned, Government has recognised that significant capital expenditure is taking place at many of the sewage treatment works of the privatised water service plcs. To regularise the situation until that work is completed (by 1992) more than 900 discharge consent conditions have been temporarily relaxed in recognition of the existing capabilities of the works concerned. Future environmental improvement is being achieved by constructing the requisite engineering works by 1992 at a cost of £1,000M or more.

5.41. With works of this magnitude and timescale being undertaken, any statistics about the number of sewage treatment works not complying with their conditions of discharge are of doubtful relevance or value. Doubtful, that is, as regards longer term environmental detriment from those discharges. The situation is compounded by the fact that the majority of water service plcs' sewage treatment works serve only small populations, and their effluent may be environmentally significant only in their immediate locality.

5.42. The basic cost of providing a sewage treatment facility is often the overriding consideration when selecting a suitable design. Many treatment plants in current operation discharge final effluents that breach existing discharge standards. Such discharges to river systems often lead to water quality levels that are a risk to river ecology and detrimental to downstream water supplies. Other sewage works discharge to marine environments often in an untreated state through obsolete short outfalls. With the increase in the loading on these discharges, beach pollution and pollution to inshore waters occurs, creating a possible public health risk to bathers and beach users, and this is widened by the growth in recreational use of inland waters. The United Kingdom has 29 blue flag beaches which pass the EC standard on beach pollution. This is less than most European countries with a similar length of coastline. The cost of cleaning beaches may be high; for example, for one major regional council in Scotland, the cost of imposing sewage treatment to reduce beach pollution is estimated to be in excess of £250M.

5.43. The table in Annex 5.A sets out the total 'sewered population' served by each of the ten water service plcs, the number of sewage treatment works in operation, and the percentage of works revealed by the then water authorities' own testing in 1986, '87, and '88 which did not comply with consent conditions. The percentage failures relate to the number of works actually tested (about 96% of all the relevant works being tested in each of the three years). A steady improvement is recorded, reflecting a combination of both capital expenditure and improved operating techniques. The table also indicates the extent to which the 'sewered population' is connected to sea outfalls in each of the regions.

5.44. The table in Annex 5.B displays the estimated level of expenditure, as set out in the 1989 Privatisation Prospectus, on sewage treatment works during the next ten years - together with details of each water service plcs expenditure on sewerage and sewage disposal, and the total expenditure on the privatised water and sewerage services as a whole over that same period. The table displays figures for sea and estuarine outfalls and also for water resource developments. The table will be referred to again in those latter specific contexts later.

5.45. The degree of pollution arising from storm and emergency overflows is difficult to quantify. Such overflows are an essential 'safety-valve' for the sewerage system insofar as their operation (by discharging into watercourses, or into estuaries and the sea) is intended to avoid having sewage overflow from manholes into streets and gardens. The generally intermittent nature of their operation renders routine monitoring of their effects difficult. Where storm conditions apply there is an attendant dilution of the discharge in the receiving water, and a natural shut-off mechanism with the discharge ceasing as the storm passes.

5.46. Pollution does arise, however, particularly when operation of an overflow is due to a blockage in the system or a mechanical failure.

Despite the need for the existence of overflows each one is a potential source of a polluting discharge. The majority of the 14,210 storm overflows referred to in the 1989 prospectus have been approved, or have temporary consents pending further consideration. Not all storm overflows may have been identified yet.

5.47. Expenditure on the improvement of the sewerage networks leading to treatment works and to sea outfalls over the next decade takes up some 23% of total estimated expenditure on water and sewerage services. Within such improvement there will be an increase (as yet unquantifiable) both in the hydraulic capacity of some existing sewerage systems and the elimination of some existing overflows. It would be uneconomic to provide piped systems and treatment works to eliminate all overflows.

5.48. In dealing with the relationship between agricultural activity and pollution of surface waters, consideration has to be given to two types of discharge. Diffuse discharges arise from the way in which surface water from agricultural land either reaches watercourses, or affects groundwater quality. The situation which gives rise to particular concern is in those parts of England where increasing concentrations of nitrate have been recorded in recent years in sources from which water is being taken for public supply.

5.49.. A general pattern has been a progressive trend of increasing nitrate concentration. In some instances levels, whilst still remaining elevated, have shown a decline from the late 1970s. However, and primarily in arable farming areas, concentrations for the period 1981-1985 were higher than those previously recorded.

5.50. The increase in nitrate concentration has been the subject of several official reports, not least in relation to the quality of groundwaters being taken for public supply.

5.51. Not all the nitrate content in water arises from agricultural activity. Nor is the leaching of nitrate entirely attributable to the application of nitrogen, in whatever form, as a fertiliser. Nevertheless Government is currently conducting trials to assess the effectiveness, and likely cost, of restricting farming practices as a longer-term way of reducing nitrate concentration and the EC is directing attention to this problem.

5.52. Agriculture also features as a potentially polluting activity because of an increasing number of individual escapes of either animal wastes or silage liquors. Both make heavy oxygen demands on receiving waters, demands which can be many times more polluting than untreated domestic sewage. Annex 5.C records incidents of pollution from agricultural and various other sources in 1986, '87 and '88. An increase in agricultural incidents of 12.5% over this period was followed in 1989 by a fall of some 30% on the 1988 figure. That welcome situation, however, may well be attributable to the dry weather prevailing during the summer rather than to any dramatic impact which policies of education and prosecution exerted within the farming community. Both policies continue to be necessary in achieving a consistent fall in the growth of reported incidents.

5.53. Pollution may also arise naturally; as during the latter part of the dry summer of 1989 when a number of reservoirs and lakes, principally in southern England, were closed temporarily to recreational use because of prolific shallow water growth of potentially toxic blue-green algae. Water supplies receiving treatment were not endangered; indeed algal growths are not unusual and appropriate treatment is available to treat the tastes they cause.

5.54. Water pollution incidents in England and Wales more than doubled between 1981 and 1988. Annex 5.C illustrates the situation for 1986, '87 and '88 and indicates the general nature of the sources of pollution. Here again the basic statistics give little guide to the impact of the pollution, but the then water authorities classified 6% of the industrial, 19% of the farm, and 3% of the sewage incidents in 1987 as serious.

5.55. Many of the incidents featuring in Annex 5.C will have originated as the result of an 'accident'. Within the water industry reaction to that situation has been twofold. Firstly, by providing as rapid a response as possible to the containment and clearing up of pollution. Secondly, by seeking to educate those responsible. Response to the accident situation will increasingly be initiated by information provided through automatic water quality monitoring technology as well as by an observant and concerned public.

5.56. 'Accident', however, can be a subjective term. In the context of water pollution it becomes stretched to include deliberate acts of vandalism, and non-compliance with procedures designed to avoid incidents occurring. In addition such other human weaknesses as error, lack of thought or knowledge, and preoccupation with other matters all feature as potential causes of accidental contamination.

5.57. Legislation, and its effective policing, brings penalty provisions to bear on accidental pollution of the kinds referred to above. It also penalises those who deliberately make unauthorised discharges. Although such penalties are applied to those who create a pollution incident legislation also provides for recovery of the costs of dealing will the effects. In the wider environmental context, however, the need to reduce the number of pollution incidents, whether arising by accident or deliberate act, is of growing importance.

5.58. It seems that there is increasing willingness to incur expenditure to ensure that consented discharges are non-polluting in their environmental effects. More insidious and longer term effects, such as with nitrate and other leachates, are still the subject of research and investigation (and are referred to again later). Accidents and deliberate acts - now subject to stringent legislation - will continue to be a threat.

Groundwaters

5.59. Surface water and groundwater are both elements of the return phase of the water cycle. Situations potentially capable of polluting surface water may equally affect groundwater. Groundwater, and the strata and aquifers through which it passes, can also become 'overloaded' by polluting substances.

5.60. There are some important differences to be taken into account. The first is that the rate at which groundwater moves, from the ground surface into the underlying strata and within an aquifer, is generally very much slower than applies to the movement of surface water. The second is that the chemical constituents of groundwater are affected by reactions between the water and the strata through which it passes. Generally, however, the concentrations do not fall within the Environmental Protection Bill's concept of the capability of causing harm to man. 'Natural' actions of this kind, however, are of a more permanent nature than those referred to in relation to surface waters. For instance, naturally occurring minerals contained within some groundwaters make them permanently unsuited for drinking, or for economic treatment to make them so.

5.61. Groundwater provides some 30% of the total public water supply in England and Wales but, south-east of a line connecting the Bristol Channel and the Humber, the proportion is significantly greater. In the South East some 74% of the public supply is groundwater derived. The most significant groundwater pollution problems are associated with the presence of nitrates, pesticides, and organic solvents. The nitrate situation only is featured here, illustrating the manner in which a hitherto cheap (relative to surface water) and reliable potable water source can be affected by contemporary situations.

5.62. The Water Quality Regulations, introduced by the 1989 Water Act, limit the concentration of nitrate in potable supplies. In those regions where sources exceed that limit the water undertakers are faced with three options; taking sources out of use, blending with water less rich in nitrate, or installing treatment plant to reduce the nitrate content. All are associated with cost to the undertaker, but are measures capable of introduction within relatively short timescales. Facilities for water treatment are being introduced by Anglian Water Services Ltd at affected sources. Some borehole supplies of the South Staffordshire Water company are also affected and the UK's first ion exchange plant for nitrate removal is being installed near Sutton Coldfield.

5.63. An alternative, and longer term, approach lies in controlling the nitrate input to both surface and groundwater systems (see paragraph 5.52 above). Such action is one specific aspect within the introduction of a deliberate policy for the general protection of aquifers, or parts of an aquifer.

5.64. The 1989 Water Act provides for the designation of water protection zones and nitrate sensitive areas to protect both surface and groundwaters. Aquifer protection looks to the location and nature of potentially polluting activities. It looks also to the physical characteristics of the aquifer, and to the location and magnitude of the abstractions being made from it.

5.65. In the context of aquifer protection all activities within 'holes in the ground' are suspect - mining, mineral extraction, wastes disposal, drainage soakaways from highways. Industrial sites, chemical storage areas, agriculture, and disposal of sewage sludges are also potential polluters.

5.66. Engineering measures, coupled with effective operation and supervision, can offer some alternative to outright prohibition or restriction. That same end might also be achieved by policies based on the power to raise charges from those gaining benefit. This could, however, mean abandoning groundwater resources to permit use of the natural capacity of an aquifer for other purposes. That would challenge attitudes based on the premise that potable water sources should be protected absolutely.

Pollution of coastal waters
Disposal of sewage sludge

5.67. Sewerage systems in developed countries handle not only human wastes but a variety of discharges, known as trade effluents, from commercial and manufacturing activities - the principle being that, with a sewerage and sewage treatment system already existing, it makes good sense to treat at least some of these non-domestic effluents at 'public' plants, rather than at their place of origin. In addition to the sewage effluent, a sewage treatment works also produces sewage sludge - a mixture of organically rich solids and water which is settled out from the sewage flow during the treatment process. Where there are trade effluents from industrial processes, however, the sludge may well also contain quantities of heavy metals.

5.68. Further consideration will be needed to reducing heavy metal concentrations in sewage sludge, in order to reduce their impact when disposal is to land or sea. A reduction in industrial waste water discharges to sewers would serve this objective. This could be achieved with the installation of closed loop production systems or by improving treatment and recovery of waste products from the waste and water system. An alternative is to review the whole concept of combined sewage systems, by reducing the quantity of clean water runoff that enters the sewers, since this creates large volumes of low concentrated effluent which are costly to treat.

5.69. Sewage sludge is not discharged with the effluent from a sewage treatment works and the extent to which it contains non-biodegradable material influences the ability to dispose of it without causing environmental harm. That situation applies whether the disposal route is to land or to sea. The EC's concept of the best available technology not entailing excessive costs (BATNEEC) applies; but, for a landlocked sewage treatment works, sea disposal has been an option requiring close consideration of the cost of transporting the sludge to a marine loading point prior to its actual disposal. The table in Annex 5.D indicates the routes by which sludges arising at sewage treatment works were disposed of in 1987 and 1988.

5.70. Some 25% of the UK's sewage sludge is currently disposed of at sea, 70% goes to land (either for landfill or for agricultural use), and 5% is incinerated. Any of these methods may present problems, real or alleged. The former tend to be related either to the contents of the sludge or to its physical consistency. Land disposal for agricultural use, for instance, is the subject of a DoE code of practice taking in the relevant EC Directive, and the UK has been under pressure for some time to cease marine disposal. In March 1990 Government announced that disposal by the marine route would be phased out by 1998.

5.71. Reference will be made shortly to the general aspects of the discharge of sewage from sea outfalls but, whilst sewage sludge is under consideration, it is pertinent to point out that a number of marine discharges are given preliminary treatment at the landward end of the outfall - producing 'screenings' which are disposed of to land. However, marine discharges are, essentially, carrying their own sludge content to the disposal point. The biodegradability of that content is thus a factor to be taken into account in relation to the environmental effects of the discharge.

5.72. Sludge produced at the UK's sewage treatment works is currently disposed of at sea (at specific and defined sites) only within the terms of licences issued, and reviewed annually, by the MAFF. In considering applications regard has been paid to protecting the marine environment and to the practicability of disposal by other means. The MAFF, reporting on the 'Disposal of Waste at Sea, 1986 and 1987' confirmed that there was 'no significant deleterious impact on the marine environment'. Licences in force in both 1986 and 1987 were: England and Wales 17; Scotland 2. The table in Annex 5.E shows the quantities of sewage sludge involved over the period 1979-1987, together with other materials to which reference is made later.

5.73. The decision to bring marine disposal to an end has been estimated to cost £320M in capital, with additional annual running costs of £30M. On the basis of the figures given in paragraph 5.70 above the quantity of sludge to be disposed either to land or by incineration will increase by some 33%. Such additional disposal may well have to be via incineration if landfill and agricultural alternatives are unavailable, and the overall effect may be to transfer problems from one environmental medium to another at increased cost.

Sewage effluent discharges

5.74. EC Directive 76/160/EEC on the quality of bathing waters led to marked changes in official attitudes in the UK. Initially only 27 beaches in England and Wales were designated as clean, on the basis of surveys made in 1979 of popular beaches and numbers of people in the water. Following a Government statement in December 1986 the UK total became 397, a figure which has continued to increase subsequently, partly due to subdivision of some bathing waters. In 1989 the total was 440 (401 in England and Wales, 23 in Scotland, and 16 in Northern Ireland). Compliance rates were 51% in 1986, 55% in 1987, 67% in 1988, and 76% in 1989.

5.75. Some 14% of the 'sewered' population of England and Wales are connected to sea outfalls. Despite work carried out by the then Regional Water Authorities after 1974, there remained an outstanding legacy of short, badly located, and physically damaged sewage outfalls discharging into coastal waters. Some £150M of capital expenditure towards making that legacy good was incurred in the four years to 1985. The rate of spend then rose to about £100M pa and is now estimated (see Annex 5.B) to average some £164M pa for the next five years falling to £81M pa between 1995 and 2000. It should be noted however that the Annex 5.B datum of November 1989 predates the 1990 decisions by Government on the discharge of sewage and sewage sludge to the sea. Overall expenditure will be significantly increased as a result of that decision.

5.76. The discharge of sewage into the sea has been seen as an economic way of dealing with a public responsibility. More enlightened thinking looked to harnessing the natural capability of the marine environment to assimilate sewage discharges after only preliminary treatment of the sewage. Proper long outfall locations secure rapid dilution of the discharge, ensure that the diluted effluent is not swept back to the shore during the assimilation process and environmental overloading of the receiving waters is avoided. The concept of the long sea outfall evolved and became the lynch pin of progress towards cleaning up the UK's coastal waters.

5.77. The development of techniques for determining effective outfall locations has progressed during the 70s and 80s, and proven engineering procedures are now readily available for placing outfalls as much as 5km from the shore. The alternative, of making use of a shorter outfall and treating the sewage flow on land, has been adopted on occasions, but good practice has been seen as lying in a choice between one or the other approach. Contemporary approaches to outfall location, design and construction are well illustrated in the South Eastern case study of the Hythe long sea outfall.

5.78. With Government's March 1990 declaration about treatment being given to all sewage effluents discharged to sea, costs variously estimated initially as lying between £2,000M and £7,000M will arise - additional to the spending programme referred to in paragraph 5.75. Prior to the March statement, the water industry in England and Wales was embarking on an estimated capital expenditure of £1,225M over ten years to provide new and replacement sea outfalls. Pollution of the UK's bathing waters by sewage discharges, on other than emergency situations, was seen as likely to be resolved by about the mid 90s, on the basis of what had hitherto been regarded, and officially endorsed, as sound practice. This planned expenditure may now need to be at least trebled, without real evidence having been produced that long sea outfalls cause significant damage to the marine environment. The extra costs incurred will represent a diversion of available resources which could otherwise be applied elsewhere in meeting other, and conceivably more urgent, environmental priorities.

Other loadings on the marine environment

5.79. Other materials, such as liquid and solid industrial wastes and dredged materials, are also disposed of at sea under licensing provisions corresponding to those referred to in paragraph 5.72 above. Such 'loadings' have attracted concern, official and otherwise, about environmental effects in the North Sea. That situation, however, is not pursued further here, other than in Annex 5.E which gave indications of the relative quantities of the materials concerned.

5.80. The description of the water cycle given earlier it will be evident that the flow of inland waters into estuaries and the sea also contributes to the loading entering the marine environment. The table in Annex 5.F indicates the UK's contribution, by weight of certain metals, to the North Sea in 1985-86 via rivers, and from other more direct sources. The contributions featured in the table which arise from continental Europe place the UK Government's March statement within a political context. It is hoped that the example set by the UK Government will stimulate other countries to corporate environmental protection activity.

5.81. In general terms some 90% of rivers in England and Wales were not a cause of extended environmental concern along their inland courses during 1986/87 and 1987/88. Whether regarded as being of 'good' or 'poor' quality, the actual loadings which they carry to the sea will be reduced as the result of the activities and expenditures described in this report.

5.82. The situation relating to the pollution of coastal waters and the sea can be summed up simply by saying that environmental pressures have brought to an end an era of cheap options for disposal. Disposal elsewhere will lead to significant expenditure - both capital and operating. The technology to effect change is generally in existence; but there may be areas where new technologies will need to be explored and developed and these are certain to be major planning battles as sites are sought for new treatment works. The community will have to assess the costs and benefits of such changes and development.

Inadequate infrastructure
Sewerage and sewage disposal

5.83. Reference has already been made to pollution arising from storm overflows on inadequate sewers; to overloaded sewage treatment works; and to unsatisfactory locations for marine sewage outfalls. The physical collapse of a number of sewers was widely reported a few years ago, with suggestions that much of the sewerage infrastructure was old and required to be replaced. Much work has since been directed at determining the physical state of water mains and sewers, the results influencing estimates of costs set out in Annex 5.B.

5.84. The table in Annex 5.B, however, makes no distinction between routine repair and maintenance work, and the more dramatic media-worthy occasions. The water service plcs are required to prepare, as part of the regulatory regime, management plans for underground assets to ensure that services are provided 'properly, economically, and efficiently'. For the ten years to 2000, expenditure on sewerage networks is some 23% of total expenditure seen as being necessary

Water supply

for effective water services at the time the privatisation prospectus was prepared. It seems unlikely that the situation will be significantly different in Scotland or Northern Ireland.

5.85. Age and inadequacies in the water supply infrastructure create less impact on the environment than do sewer problems. Customers are inconvenienced, but the environment is affected, if at all, only locally and for a short time. There is an exception to this, however, if sustained over-abstraction from a water source cause surface water flows to become depleted.

5.86. In some cases over-abstraction might well be laid at the door of the increasing demand for piped water supplies. A 6% increase was recorded for England and Wales over the eight years between 1974 and 1981, but demand in earlier years was rising more rapidly: 20% over the eight years between 1966 and 1973, and 38% over the thirteen years from 1961.

5.87. Some of this increased 'demand' was, in fact, leakage arising within an ageing distribution system and the advent of the 80's saw increasing effort being made not only to reduce leakage, but to conserve existing supplies by such measures as dual (and reduced) flush WC cisterns, spray taps, and the metering of some individual supplies. The final column of the table in Annex 5.B indicates the relatively small proportion (4.4%) of total expenditure between 1990 and 2000 seen as being required for new sources of water supply. Account has also to be taken, however, of demands being met by the 'water supply only' element of the water industry in England and Wales.

5.88. That, however, is only part of the over-abstraction story because, as indicated in paragraph 5.16, new abstractions became subject to licensing from the mid 1960s; the purpose being both to ensure that resources were available to meet new demands, and to prevent their over-exploitation. This twofold approach resulted in new thinking being applied to water resource developments, to the manner in which the abstractions supporting them were licensed, and to the way such new schemes were operated on a day-to-day basis. The Midlands Case Study of the Shropshire Groundwater Scheme has enabled increased demand for water to be met without causing significant environmental impact.

5.89. The study of six chalk streams flowing to the Thames typifies the situations associated with allegedly depleted flows. Remedial works were estimated to cost £12M in 1988 (with wide variation around the average). There are parallels in other river catchments in the UK; full identification of potential costs now becomes a matter for the National Rivers Authority, introducing 'who does/who pays' considerations. The excessive use of groundwater, in some instances, leads to the deterioration of countryside amenities such as ponds, streams, and small rivers, which are then less able to dilute surface run off. The NRA are resolved to restore flow to rivers dried by over abstraction from unconfined aquifers, while continuing to satisfy the increasing per capita demand for water.

5.90. The obverse face of the situation just referred to has become evident beneath London, where rising groundwater levels present a longer term (20-30 years) threat to the stability of underground structures and building foundations.

5.91. During the past two centuries the pumping of water from the deep aquifer beneath London has reduced groundwater levels by as much as

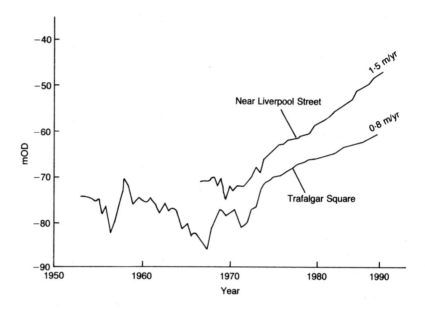

Figure 5.2. Rise in aquifer levels at two places in Central London. Reproduced with permission of CIRIA (the Construction Industry Research & Information Association) from "The engineering implications of rising groundwater levels in the deep aquifer beneath London (SP 69, Fig. 2)

70m. Reduced abstraction, reflecting decreased use of the aquifer from about 1970 onwards, is causing the level to rise by about 1m/year (see Figure 5.2). Corresponding situations have been observed in Birmingham and Liverpool.

5.92. A postulated solution, again creating a 'who does/who pays' situation, would be to pump at a number of locations to control the groundwater level. Capital costs were estimated, on a preliminary basis, in 1988 at some £10M-£30M (operating costs some £3M pa), against potential building damage of many £M. This problem requires further assessment and (if the outcome is as suggested) the construction of the necessary infrastructure.

Reservoir construction

5.93. The construction of impounding reservoirs raises issues concerning impact upon the environment - both local to the site and in terms of the more remotely experienced effects of the actual impoundment. Construction periods of several years are usual. Local physical effects, common to large engineering projects, are to be expected, irrespective of the manner in which abstraction and retention of water may produce downstream effects. Local physical effects, common to all engineering projects, are to be expected quite irrespective of the manner in which the abstraction of water, and its retention in a reservoir, may produce long term effects downstream. Environmental considerations of this kind feature in the two case studies from Edinburgh and East of Scotland Association, the Megget reservoir and River Earn water supply scheme.

5.94. Under EC Directive 85/337/EEC reservoirs would be subject to environmental assessment if their size or location is likely to have significant effects. Relative to the costs of reservoir scheme construction, any measures for protecting either the local or the more remote environment are likely to be of small cost in the UK.

67

5.95. Reservoirs storing water above ground level in the UK are, for safety reasons, subject to legislation requiring that their design, supervision, and regular inspection be carried out by specifically qualified engineers. Many reservoirs in the upland areas of the North and West are over 75 years old and have long ceased to be regarded as an environmental intrusion. The structural condition of any reservoir may, however, call for engineering works at relatively short notice, with attendant short term effects locally and, possibly, on the more remote environment should impounded water become temporarily unavailable to maintain downstream flows.

5.96. Summarising in relation to inadequate infrastructure, it has to be appreciated that neither structures nor water cycle operating systems can be expected to fulfil their functions without need for regular 'maintenance' and, occasionally, replacement. Where inadequacies arise within the water cycle which have implications either for safety or for the environment action should not be delayed. In many areas responsibility for acting, and for meeting the resultant expenditure, is well defined; where it is not, resolution of responsibility is an urgent necessity and should be put in hand by Government.

Summary

5.97. Water and the water cycle are part of a life support system upon which man, amongst other forms of life, is totally dependent. If subjected to pollution the water cycle has a natural assimilative and self-healing capacity, providing always that the degree and nature of the pollution does not overtax that natural capability.

5.98. Man is able to apply technology in augmenting that natural capability; but, having also exploited the water cycle in pursuit of economic wealth, more of that wealth now needs to be directed into such assistance. In that way the intrinsically renewable resource can be preserved and its use continued.

5.99. Particularly during the past two centuries the capabilities of that resource have been overtaxed, causing deterioration of the water environment to varying degrees. That situation of decline often lasted for several decades before perception of what was happening emphasised the need to harness both technology and legislation to the process of control and recovery.

5.100. Recovery is dependent on investment - currently exemplified by the commitment of the UK's water industry to incur heavy expenditure over at least a decade on infrastructure renewal, the cleaning-up of estuarine and coastal waters, and the statutory application of a variety of water quality requirements to piped supplies.

5.101. Such expenditure, however, has to come from the pockets of those served by the water industry. The call for more environmental sensitivity is likely to be thwarted by lack of will to fund, rather than by technology being unable to provide the necessary works.

5.102. The water cycle is a vital part of the natural environment, but cannot be isolated from other components of that environment. Within the UK in the past 25 years there has been a growing commitment to both the principle and the practice of coordinated river basin management. There is now a need to extend both the principle and the practice beyond the water cycle and into a wider environmental field.

5.103. The Institution believes that a national body, covering all aspects of the environmental pollution situation, is now required. In the absence of such a body it is likely that investment and action cannot be fully effective. Given the complexity of environmental issues the arguments for an Environmental Protection Agency are very strong.

5.104. Supporting the principle of 'the polluter pays' the Institution nevertheless recognises that the totality of environmental protection investment can be met only if some costs fall upon the wider community which benefits from the protection of water.

5.105. Within the UK's water environment the three factors of awareness, legislation, and investment now make it possible to expect that consented effluent discharges will become non-polluting (except in emergency situations). Accidents and deliberate acts of non-compliance present a threat against which constant vigilance, and rapid action, will be required.

5.106. Leachates (i.e. nitrates, wastes disposal effluents) present a continuing threat to groundwaters in particular, and are the subject of research and action. Because pollution is slow to be eradicated the protection of groundwater needs to be a matter of high priority. It is possible, however, that it may be necessary to accept a small number of aquifers becoming or remaining polluted to a degree beyond that which is assimilable.

5.107. Protection of the water environment calls for heavy, and continuing expenditure based upon clear priorities. The Institution urges that priorities are based on scientific evidence, particularly where established actions have been monitored and hitherto have been held to be in accord with good environmental practice.

5.108. Engineering structures within the water cycle often have a long life, but nevertheless a finite one. Where the responsibility for operation, inspection, and maintenance is defined there are few grounds for apprehension about either public safety or environmental protection. There are some areas (rising groundwater, over-authorisation of abstraction, responsibility for abandoned works), however, where existing organisations may have to accept added responsibilities if harmful effects are to be avoided.

ANNEX 5.A.

Sewered population in England and Wales

Water service company	Population (x1000)			Number of sewage treatment works	Percentage (%) of works tested not complying with consent conditions		
	Resident	Sewage treatment works	Sea outfalls		1986	1987	1988
1	2	3	4	5	6	7	8
Anglian	5352	4442	445	1091	40	34	28
Northumbrian	2568	1669	889	435	19	15	15
North West	6779	5219	1451	643	14	12	10
Severn Trent	8199	7953	nil	1063	23	22	15
Southern	4000	2426	1574	393	19	14	15
Southwest	1478	798	464	610	29	30	30
Thames	11561	11329	nil	398	18	18	16
Welsh	3061	1653	1320	894	17	18	17
Wessex	2417	1982	277	359	14	11	6
Yorkshire	4650	4092	410	637	23	21	17
England & Wales	**50100**	**41563** (82.9%)	**6830** (13.5%)	**6523**	**23**	**21**	**17**

Sources: Waterfacts 1988 (columns 2-4); Prospectus: The Water Share Offers - November 1989 (column 5); Hansard 19 May 1989 (columns 6-8)

ANNEX 5.B.

Estimated programmed expenditure £M (November 1989 prices)

Water service company		Privatised water and sewerage services	Sewage treatment		Sea and estuarine outfalls		Sewerage and sewage treatment services		Privatised water resource development	
1		2	3		4		5		6	
Anglian	1990/1995	1470	380	(25.8)	60	(4.1)	680	(46.2)	20	(1.4)
	1995/2000	1990	470	(23.6)	130	(6.5)	1050	(52.8)	20	(1.0)
Northumbrian	1990/1995	540	140	(25.9)	80	(14.8)	350	(64.8)	10	(1.8)
	1995/2000	345	55	(15.9)	15	(15.9)	175	(50.7)	0	
North West	1990/1995	2220	320	(14.4)	190	(8.5)	1100	(49.5)	115	(5.2)
	1995/2000	2060	390	(18.9)	65	(3.1)	975	(47.3)	2060	(5.8)
Severn Trent	1990/1995	2330	630	(27.0)		0	1050	(45.1)	50	(2.1)
	1995/2000	1750	370	(21.1)		0	760	(43.4)	40	(2,3)
Southern	1990/1995	830	180	(21.7)	250	(30.1)	565	(68.1)	60	(7.2)
	1995/2000	500	205	(41.0)	25	(5.0)	320	(64.0)	35	(7.0)
South West	1990/1995	765	160	(20.9)	120	(15.7)	440	(57.5)	25	(3.2)
	1995/2000	525	80	(15.2)	95	(18.1)	315	(60.0)	10	(1.9)
Thames	1990/1995	1890	495	(26.2)		0	925	(48.9)	110	(5.8)
	1995/2000	1920	400	(20.8)		0	955	(49.7)	210	(10.9)
Welsh	1990/1995	880	140	(15.9)	70	(7.9)	395	(44.9)	10	(1.1)
	1995/2000	875	65	(7.4)	70	(5.7)	285	(32.6)	20	(2.3)
Wessex	1990/1995	650	155	(23.8)	30	(4.6)	430	(66.1)	30	(4.6)
	1995/2000	625	125	(20.0)	15	(2.4)	405	(64.8)	40	(6.4)
Yorkshire	1990/1995	1210	340	(28.1)	20	(1.6)	590	(48.8)	60	(4.9)
	1995/2000	1210	180	(14.9)	10	(0.8)	470	(38.8)	110	(9.0)
England & Wales	1990/1995	12 785	2940	(23.0)	820	(6.4)	6525	(51.0)	490	(3.8)
	1995/2000	11 800	2340	(19.8)	405	(3.4)	5710	(48.4)	605	(5.1)

(Figures in brackets represent percentage of overall figures set out in column 2)

Source: Prospectus: The Water Share Offers - November 1989

ANNEX 5.C.

Reported water pollution incidents

Water service company		Agricultural	Industrial	Sewage and sewerage	Other	Total
Anglian	1986	275	654	380	159	1468
	1987	223	783	381	218	1605
	1988	203	647	373	223	1446
Northumbrian	1986	62	252	262	153	729
	1987	94	170	232	122	618
	1988	80	201	273	141	695
North West	1986	456	623	464	358	1901
	1987	539	830	460	427	2256
	1988	612	846	614	495	2567
Severn Trent	1986	579	2155	896	867	4497
	1987	654	1863	880	1038	4435
	1988	582	2408	772	1530	5292
Southern	1986	174	694	314	414	1596
	1987	189	664	320	496	1669
	1988	1120	641	345	409	1515
South West	1986	830	470	435	340	2075
	1987	666	460	427	371	1924
	1988	840	595	488	463	2386
Thames	1986	151	1147	354	340	2523
	1987	182	1051	423	586	2242
	1988	188	1579	610	997	3374
Welsh	1986	412	404	348	455	1619
	1987	716	370	402	1001	2489
	1988	582	550	476	577	2185
Wessex	1986	328	407	416	210	1091
	1987	271	445	129	251	1096
	1988	392	595	168	506	1661
Yorkshire	1986	246	923	538	459	2166
	1987	336	939	523	525	2323
	1988	353	1023	459	698	2533
England & Wales	1986	3513	7729	4137	4286	19,665
	1987	3870	7575	4177	5017	20,639
	1988	3952	9085	4578	6039	23,654

Source: Waterfacts 1987, Waterfacts 1988 and Digest of Environmental Protection and Water Statistics 1989.

ANNEX 5.D.

Disposal of dry solids

Water service company		Thousand tonnes dry solids disposed to:				Total 1000 tonnes dry solids
		farmland	landfill	sea	incinerator	
Anglian	1987	94	16	15	0	125
	1988	97	9	16	0	122
Northumbrian	1987	8	12	24	0	44
	1988	9	9	17	0	35
North West	1987	32	19	67	6	124
	1988	28	25	61	6	120
Severn Trent	1987	90	60	0	30	180
	1988	82	63	0	30	175
Southern	1987	34	7	9	3	53
	1988	37	10	9	3	59
South West	1987	10	1	4	0	15
	1988	9	1	4	0	14
Thames	1987	77	8	93	0	178
	1988	140	10	100	0	250
Welsh	1987	23	5	12	0	40
	1988	20	0	10	0	30
Wessex	1987	30	3	9	0	42
	1988	29	3	10	0	42
Yorkshire	1987	53	51	8	10	122
	1988	55	33	5	14	107
England and Wales	1987	451	168	239	41	900
	1988	506	163	232	53	954

Source: Waterfacts 1988 and 1989

ANNEX 5.E.

Dumping of materials at sea by the UK

Material	1979	1980	1981	1982	Million tonnes 1983	1984	1985	1876	1987	1988
Sewage sludge (wet weight)	8.5	8.9	8.5	8.1	7.3	7.5	7.5	8.0	7.3	7.2
Industrial waste (including colliery wastes and flyash)	2.9	2.5	2.5	2.2	2.5	0.7	2.0	2.2	2.2	2.3
Dredgings	12.1	16.0	12.8	12.9	12.7	20.2	12.5	15.2	13.0	9.1

Source: Digest of Environmental Protection & Water Statistics 1989

ANNEX 5.F.

Annual input of metals to the North Sea from the UK

	Inputs to the North Sea from the UK (Tonnes pa 1985-1986)							Total from all countries
Substance	Rivers min. max.		Direct	Dredgings	Sewage sludge	Industrial (liquid)	Industrial (solid)	Incineration at sea	(excluding atmospheric inputs)
Cadmium	8	14	16	5	3	<1	<1	<1	90
Mercury	4	5	3	5	1	<1	<1	<1	40
Copper	240	283	215	262	103	1	160	<1	2700
Lead	245	303	133	338	99	1	206	<1	3500
Zinc	1440	1451	986	970	219	5	396	<1	17000
Chromium	98	141	439	453	39	<1	16	<1	4000
Nickel	233	265	88	117	14	<1	51	<1	1150
Arsenic	28	65	220		<1	38	4	<1	800

Source: Digest of Environmental Protection & Water Statistics 1988

6. Waste disposal

6.1.   'Burn your rubbish and save your rates' was the slogan painted on the sides of many dust-carts in the 1930s. The rubbish that was not burnt by the householder was collected by the local council and either burnt in a somewhat basic incinerator, which poured its clouds of dust and smoke into the atmosphere or, alternatively, dumped into an open tip which was sited usually not far from the urban fringe, or in some cases within it.

6.2.   Industrial wastes were dealt with similarly. Admittedly these wastes were less than at the present time in quantity, complexity and toxicity. If liquid they were usually discharged into the sewerage system or a conveniently sited watercourse and, if solid, dumped on a tip which was often on land acquired for that particular purpose by the factory owner and frequently within the premises of the factory.

6.3.   Public health and planning controls were virtually non-existent as was the public awareness of what it was doing to the environment, and the legacy that was being left for future generations.

6.4.   The change from the 'laissez-faire' attitudes of the 1930s to the present concern for the protection of the environment has been a slow one, until recent years when there has been an enormous increase in environmental awareness. There is, however, still a long way to go, not only in the field of educating the public and developing further the social conscience but in the research into methods of ensuring that the adverse effect of human activities on the environment is minimised.

6.5.   The Public Health (Drainage of Trade Premises) Act of 1937 was a major step forward. It empowered local authorities to impose conditions on any proposed discharge of industrial waste into public sewers. These conditions could specify limits relating to temperature, acidity, quantity, solid content, period of discharge and so on but it did nothing to deal with existing discharges. The Act, however, often resulted in pretreatment of effluent being carried out prior to discharge into the sewer, thus avoiding adverse effects both on the sewerage systems and the treatment process at the sewage works. The ultimate result of this was the prevention, to a great degree, of further pollution of streams and rivers.

6.6.   The Town and County Planning Act 1947 included tipping in its all embracing definition of development, for which planning permission had to be obtained.   The grant of planning permission could be accompanied by such conditions as the planning authority considered necessary to minimise, within reason, any adverse impact on the environment. Although, in the early days of the Act conditions, in many cases, tended to be minimal the powers were there to impose more severe conditions if required, and these powers have not changed in principle in subsequent planning legislation.

6.7.   Many acts of Parliament have dealt with, or touched on, aspects of pollution whether of land, water, or air but the Control of Pollution Act 1974 was a major step forward in extending the controls which could be applied to, among other things, waste, the term rubbish having been superseded. 'Tips' had become 'landfill sites' operating under licences granted by 'waste disposal authorities' as the county councils had become in England and the district councils in Wales. The conditions of the licences are enforced by waste disposal officers in England, who are civil engineers or chemists usually responsible to the county surveyor, whilst in Wales enforcement is the responsibility of environmental health officers, the successors in title to the former sanitary inspectors. The Institute of Public Cleansing, after a couple of name changes, became The Institute of Waste Management. Waste had become big business in both the public and private sectors. The technical and financial resources devoted to waste disposal increased enormously and this has borne fruit. Landfill sites are now being professionally designed and managed usually by civil engineers in close association with other disciplines including chemists, bacteriologists and geologists.

6.8. Disused mineral workings such as quarries, opencast coal sites, and gravel pits became valuable resources as potential landfill sites and tipping in disused mineral workings on lowlying sites of poor quality was termed 'land reclamation'. The case studies include a number of examples of land reclamation projects in which disused waste land has been revitalised, e.g. Lochore Meadows, Ebbw Vale Garden Festival and the Esso Service Station on the M25.

6.9. The waste problem, particularly in developed countries, has changed considerably since the 1930s. At that time domestic refuse had an appreciable ash content from coal burning fires and the quantity of packaging and food tins was not great.

6.10. At the present time the ash content, due to the advent of oil and gas fired central heating, is generally almost nil but the enormous increase in packaging of both foods and consumer goods has increased the organic content, mainly paper and board, considerably and the use of plastics, mainly of the non-biodegradable type, have created further problems.

6.11. This present day domestic waste, though probably not less in weight, is much less dense than the rubbish of half a century ago and, when disposed of by the landfill, takes much longer to compact and settle. The scale of landfill sites has increased and the importance of the solution of any methane or water problem has increased the need for after care. One result of this is that a much longer time elapses than the former 12-20 years before the site can be used for permanent beneficial development. It can, of course, be landscaped and used for recreational purposes, agriculture or open storage in the intervening period, provided landfill gas control is achieved.

6.12. In the industrial field, manufacturing processes have become more sophisticated requiring a greater diversity and increased quantities of new chemicals and radioactive substances producing wastes which, unless disposed of in a safe manner, can have a damaging effect on the environment by polluting land and watercourses.

Waste

6.13. There are many ways of classifying waste. The Control of Pollution Act 1974 refers to controlled waste which includes industrial, commercial and household waste. Commercial waste is mainly organic consisting of paper, board, packaging from shops and offices and also waste from food shops, hotels and restaurants. In the packaging element there is a certain amount of plastic material little of which is biodegradable.

6.14. The Act also refers to special waste which is a potential danger to life having corrosive, toxic or flammable properties. This generally has its origins in industry and may require special treatment for its safe disposal, or even pre-treatment before it leaves the factory of its origin. These industrial wastes may be sludges which contain substances in solution and suspension.

6.15. Medical waste also requires special treatment. This emanates mainly from hospitals but some comes from doctor's surgeries and may contain drugs, human tissue, infected swabs, hypodermic needles and similar matter. This waste is usually incinerated and, in many cases hospitals have their own incinerators to deal with it. Compared with other wastes the quantities of this are relatively small.

6.16. Difficult wastes is a term given to those wastes that are difficult to handle and may require specialised disposal techniques. These range from hazardous wastes such as those classified as Special to bulky items such as car and lorry tyres. All liquid and sludge wastes are classified as difficult. The case study at Inverness illustrates the use of waste tyres to construct a coastal protection wall.

6.17. Waste from the construction industry, especially excavated material is used on landfill sites to cover waste, particularly domestic waste, as soon as possible after it has been deposited. This contains the refuse, prevents paper being blown about the site and reduces possible nuisance from smell and flies in summer.

6.18. Industrial waste covers a wide variety of materials from inert materials to highly toxic chemicals such as acids, cyanides, dioxins and PCBs. In between these are organic wastes from furniture factories and food processing which will decompose, and chemicals which can easily be rendered innocuous at source.

6.19. Nuclear waste is a recent problem in waste disposal and arises mainly from the decommissioning of nuclear power stations. Until the material appeared in appreciable quantities the only similar wastes were such things as radioactive isotopes used in medicine and also in industry, but the quantities were so small that no particular problem occurred in their disposal.

6.20. The average household produces about a tonne of domestic refuse each year and, although this has probably changed little over past decades, the lesser ash content has been compensated for by the increased packaging and disposable materials of lower density. This has

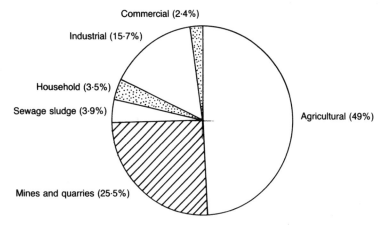

Figure 6.1. Estimated total annual waste in the late 1980s (total 500 M tonnes). Source: DoE (Excludes liquid industrial effluent of approximately 2,000 M tonnes).

considerably increased the volume of domestic refuse for disposal.

6.21. Much waste is disposed of by the private sector, particulary waste generated by industry. These waste disposal contractors have their own landfill sites and, where necessary, more sophisticated plant to ensure safe disposal of the more dangerous wastes.

6.22. These sources of waste account for about one-third of the total waste produced. The other two-thirds arise from agriculture and mineral workings, mainly coal, both mined and opencast, and quarrying. Much of this is dealt with in the vicinity of its point of origin, the disposal of mineral waste being in accordance with any conditions imposed when planning permission was granted, agricultural activities being largely exempt. Approximately half of all waste being landfilled comes from the construction industry.

Methods of disposal

6.23. The UK produces an estimated 28M+ tonnes of domestic waste annually, together with 52M tonnes of commercial and industrial wastes. Many countries consider landfilling to be a relatively safe, cheap and environmentally acceptable means of disposal for large quantities of domestic, commercial and non-toxic wastes. In Japan, where land is in short supply and very expensive, over two-thirds of all domestic refuse is incinerated, leaving only around 30% to go to landfill. By comparison, over 90% of all controlled waste in the UK is landfilled.

6.24. Landfills require careful planning, engineering design and operational control in order to minimise the effect on the environment. There is a need for the civil engineer to play an increasingly major role in the design and development of such sites, which can often involve large scale earthworks and extensive drainage, water management and infrastructure elements.

6.25. In Western Europe some 90% of all waste is disposed of in landfill sites. In the UK, these operations are carried out under conditions imposed by the planning authority, when it grants planning permission, and also by the waste disposal authority when it issues a site licence.

6.26. The planning conditions relate mainly to site access, levels and contours to which tipping is carried out, staging of the work, interim and final restoration of the site and similar matters.

6.27. The site licence has dealt more with operational matters, programming of work, prevention of nuisance from rats, flies, seagulls, noise, smell and windblown paper, hours of operation, site management, records and similar matters. The licence is increasingly being used to control boreholes for water, gas monitoring and control, and the engineering methods, such as lining and capping of the site, required to ensure there is no pollution. Even the level of supervision by chemists and engineers is included.

6.28. Landfill is generally the cheapest method of waste disposal. It can cost as little as £5 per tonne, but costs such as these vary greatly due to the cost of land acquisition, site preparation, operating conditions and so on. Licensing and planning conditions are generally more stringent where landfill sites are in prominent positions or close to urban areas. These and site factors can increase the cost to £12 - £15 per tonne or even more.

6.29. Incineration is used to a small extent. This process reduces the volume of refuse by 75% and leaves a clinker ash to be disposed of by landfill. This ash, having had its organic content destroyed in the incineration process is inert and will not support plant life to any great extent. Incineration is not without its problems of dust, noise and smoke which occur from time to time even in the most stringently controlled plants. This process can cost £25 or more per tonne.

6.30. Special wastes may require special treatment, metals, metallic compounds and chemicals can contaminate landfill sites and, in some cases, can inhibit plant life or be absorbed by plants causing problems if consumed by animals or human beings. The principal problem metals involve lead, zinc, iron, copper, mercury, aluminium and cadmium, whilst the chemicals can involve strong acids or alkalis and cyanides. Some chemicals can be rendered relatively harmless by pre-treatment at the place of origin. This pre-treatment can include neutralising acids with alkalis, utilising chemical re-agents, or flocculating agents to precipitate solids in suspension.

6.31. Other chemicals require more sophisticated treatments, PCBs, dioxins and some other dangerous chemicals comprising about 2% of all hazardous waste, require incineration at high and carefully controlled temperatures. This can cost up to a £1,000 per tonne to deal with satisfactorily.

6.32. About 8% of hazardous waste is disposed of by dumping at sea. This cannot be regarded as a satisfactory method of dealing with this type of waste even though it is subject to very strict conditions. Under proposed legislation additional powers are being sought to control this form of disposal even more closely, and it is proposed to increase the maximum penalty for infringements from the present £2,000 to £50,000.

6.33. Domestic waste collection is an integral part of the disposal process and cannot, in economic terms, be considered in isolation. The cost of disposing of waste includes the cost of collection and also the cost of transportation to the disposal site as well as the cost of actual disposal.

6.34. Where the cost of transport to a distant landfill site is high, it may be less costly to use the more expensive incineration process on a site nearer to the source of the refuse if the lesser transport costs outweigh the additional costs of incineration.

6.35. Where a landfill site is distant, transport costs may be reduced by compacting the refuse into bales or in specially designed large trailers. Alternatively, where distances are greater than 8 - 10 miles refuse may be transferred to bulk containers at a transfer station for conveyance to its final destination. This is usually more economical than using the collection vehicles, with their crew, to travel excessive distances to disposal facilities. The problems of refuse disposal in Edinburgh were solved by transporting the city's refuse by rail to landfill sites - the Powderhall case study.

Landfill

6.36. Landfill is the cheapest method of waste disposal and, apart from the aspect of land reclamation, does, in theory, return to the earth the elements abstracted from it. This method is used mainly for the disposal of controlled waste, that is domestic, commercial and inert or organic industrial wastes, although it is also used in some locations for the disposal of special wastes.

6.37. Domestic refuse varies in content with geographical location and the season of the year but a typical analysis is shown in Figure 6.2. The two largest items, paper and board and perishable matter (mainly food etc.), are organic and will decompose over a period of time to form, along with the dust and grit, a soil which will support plant life.

6.38. The basic method of operating a landfill site is to tip the refuse in layers of up to 2m in thickness, compact it with heavy plant and cover with soil as the tipping proceeds. At the end of each day the tip face should also be covered. This contains the refuse in a number of cells which limits the spread of an underground fire should it occur. The covering of the tip as work proceeds also limits the possibility of nuisance from seagulls, flies, smells and windblown paper as well as reducing the adverse visual impact of the operation. Seagulls feed on the refuse and are a particular nuisance, if the site is near a residential area or in the vicinity of an airport, where there is a risk of a bird being ingested into an aircraft engine with potentially disastrous results. Flies and smells are an occasional minor problem during hot summers, and can be dealt with by spraying should they occur. Increasingly the Regulatory Authority will require a plan of operation engineered to avoid pollution. Successful plans will be the result of multidisciplinary co-operation of engineers, chemists, biologists and geologists.

6.39. The more serious problems associated with landfill sites are the long term ones arising from the generation of gases and liquids from the decomposing waste. The gases are primarily methane (CH_4) and to a lesser extent carbon dioxide (CO_2), hydrogen sulphide (H_2S) and carbon monoxide (CO).

6.40. In a mixture with air, methane can form an explosive combination which can give rise to potentially hazardous conditions. Carbon dioxide is heavier than air and can collect in manholes in the site drainage system and, unless normal precautions are taken, can cause suffocation. Hydrogen sulphide and carbon monoxide are toxic, but do not appear in large quantities or give rise to major problems. Hydrogen sulphide, however, has a most unpleasant smell of rotten eggs. The main smell in landfill is from trace organics, e.g. organo-sulphur compounds.

6.41. The liquid problem is caused by polluted water, called leachate, draining from the decomposing refuse. Leachate carries chemicals in solution and partly decomposed organic particles in suspension.

6.42. The most obvious problems of a badly planned landfill site are often its visual impact on the environment during its operation and, unless properly restored after its completion. However, good engineering can design out most of the problems.

6.43. Pulverisation of refuse can be carried out prior to depositing it on the landfill site. This process chops up the refuse into small pieces and starts off the decomposition process. When deposited on the landfill site it resembles a coarse homogeneous soil, which causes little

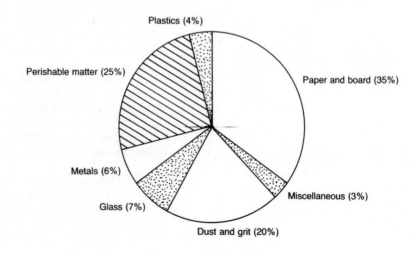

Figure 6.2. Domestic refuse content. Source: DoE

visual intrusion into the landscape, has no large papers to blow about, requires cover material only for water balance, and in the long term consolidates evenly. The process could cost an additional £10 - £15 over normal landfill but this is partly offset by savings in not having to import cover material and also the longer life of the tip which is not used up by this cover material.

6.44. A controlled amount of certain industrial wastes, as solids or sludges, can often be disposed of on landfill sites used for domestic refuse without any adverse effect. This is known as codisposal.

6.45. Sewage sludge may also, with advantage, be disposed of on landfill sites and this composting process adds humus and valuable trace elements to the refuse which enhances the value of the soil produced by the decomposition process.

6.46. Visual intrusion during the operational life of a landfill site can be minimised by screening, landscaping and close control of the tipping operation.

6.47. As stages of the landfill site are completed the surface may need to be capped with at least 1m of compacted clay before covering and the area landscaped, which, to be satisfactory, should have been designed prior to the start of the landfill operation, in order to achieve the necessary contouring of the site as tipping proceeds. A good example of the landscaping of a landfill site is Otterspool Promenade in Liverpool. A sea wall of 6m high was constructed along the frontage of the Mersey Estuary and the area behind, filled with refuse and landscaped. A paved promenade was constructed together with the creation of grass areas for recreation, shrubberies and flowerbeds.

6.48. It appears probable that landfill will be the principal method of waste disposal for many years to come. Although landfill sites are normally only planned for 10 - 20 years ahead it does appear that there will be adequate facilities for many years beyond that period.

6.49. Some opencast coal sites already offer 80 - 100 years tipping space at the present rate. There are many existing quarries and sites where mineral extraction, mainly coal and iron, have taken place which are available for landfill and the development of new sites will offer further opportunities.

6.50. Gravel pits are likely to be unsuitable as gravel seams offer rapid routes for the dispersion of leachate and this could cause pollution of potential water supplies at considerable distances from the gravel workings. Such pits may need to be clay lined, and the engineering problems require soil mechanics design.

6.51. Low lying land can be borrowed, its levels raised and, on completion of landfill operations, returned to agricultural use. The possibilities of this are considerable.

6.52. It appears, therefore, that there are sufficient potential landfill sites to cope with this method of disposal for the foreseeable future, even if there is no change in the quantities of refuse produced. These quantities, however, may well reduce if more materials are reclaimed and recycled. Other measures mentioned in this report, if accepted, would further reduce the quantity of waste for disposal.

6.53. Although there are sufficient landfill sites, these are not always in the most convenient locations and waste, therefore, may have to be transported considerable distances. For example waste from the South East of England is being transported to Bedfordshire for disposal in worked out clay pits.

6.54. Where long distances are involved, British Rail has developed a service, by which regular shipments of waste are transported, by the trainload and at regular intervals, to distant sites for final disposal.

Leachate

6.55. This liquid, which can emanate from landfill sites, can pollute watercourses and underground aquifers, potential sources of drinking water, unless adequate precautions are taken in the original design of the landfill site. Such precautions are part of a multidisciplinary design of the site. If the leachate is a pollutant then it will require engineering to

(a) prevent rain water flowing into the site by drainage of clean water around the sites
(b) sealing of the bottom and sides to prevent ingress or egress
(c) a series of cells separated by clay bunds to prevent polluting of clean areas by leachate within the site.

6.56. Leachate consists of water which must not be allowed to flow from the site carrying with it, in solution or suspension, chemicals, metal contaminants and organic matter. Care is needed to ensure that this leachate is not discharged into watercourses but some, or all, may percolate through the ground to underground aquifers. The main problem is generally caused by the continuing decomposition of the suspended organic matter which absorbs oxygen in this process. This oxygen requirement, known as the Biological Oxygen Demand (BOD) is one measure of the 'strength' of the leachate.

6.57. If any leachate is discharged into a watercourse, it will absorb oxygen from the water to satisfy this demand and complete its decomposition, and unless the dilution is such that the watercourse can cope with this demand, the level of oxygen in the water can fall below that necessary to support fish and animal life and these will suffocate. In extreme circumstances, the levels can drop below that necessary to support plant life with disastrous results. A further problem which can occur is the production of ammonia which can also adversely affect fish and plant life.

6.58. As far as underground aquifers are concerned, these are potential sources of drinking water, unless they already hold saline water. In sandstones attenuation of the leachate occurs as it percolates through the rock thus lessening possible pollution but in formations of fissured rock, such as chalk or limestone, leachate can flow into the aquifers virtually unchanged except, perhaps, for some dilution by groundwater.

6.59. By reducing the amount of water gaining access to the landfill site, the volume of leachate is reduced. The organic matter has a longer period to decompose within the site itself, therefore tending to reduce the BOD of the resulting leachate as well as its volume.

6.60. Water is prevented from entering the site from adjacent land by the provision of suitable cut off drains along appropriate sections of the landfill site perimeter. On completion of a stage of landfill, the provision of a suitably contoured layer of clay over the surface will prevent, to a large extent, rain penetrating into the waste. Engineering design must be carried out to ensure a water balance.

6.61. Where these measures prove inadequate to produce a leachate of an acceptable standard, the leachate can be collected in a lagoon for treatment, such as bubbling compressed air through the liquid from diffusers at the bottom of the lagoon.

6.62. The generation of leachate from landfill sites continues for many years after tipping has ceased, and treatment must not cease with the closing of the site. The composition of the leachate changes over time, hence treatment may need to change.

Methane

6.63. Methane or marsh gas is produced during the decomposition of organic refuse and a mixture with air comprising 5% - 14% of methane forms an explosive mixture. Apart from any potential hazard on the site, the gas can migrate underground and collect in areas away from the landfill site giving rise to potential hazards where they would not be anticipated.

6.64. The potential for methane generation has increased over recent decades due to the increased organic content of domestic refuse. The rate of production, which varies with time is affected by a number of factors including the degree of compaction, temperature and moisture content.

6.65. If refuse is lightly compacted, such as by the bulldozers placing the material, the refuse contains air voids and decomposition, which is a bacteriological process, and is carried out by aerobic bacteria (that is bacteria requiring oxygen). Some methane is produced which percolates to the surface and is dissipated into the atmosphere. This cannot be relied upon as the only method of control.

6.66. Where heavy mechanical compaction takes place the volume of air voids in the refuse is greatly reduced and anaerobic decomposition takes place (that is by bacteria which do not require oxygen). This process, assisted by higher temperatures due to heat generated in the tipped material, accelerates the production of methane. This methane may need attention, such as flaring off on the surface, if the quantities are appreciable, particularly where there is a considerable depth of tipped material and especially if the refuse is clay capped which would inhibit its dissipation into the atmosphere and assist its migration to adjacent sites.

6.67. As with leachate, the generation of methane will continue for many years after the landfill site has ceased to be operational. Leicestershire County Council have successfully controlled the release of methane and are collecting the gas as a resource at Enderby (case study).

6.68. Control and re-use of methane on landfill sites is of prime importance, since methane gas mixture in air can, under certain circumstances, form an explosive mixture, which has the power to inflict heavy physical damage and loss of life within 250m of landfill area and for 15-25 years after waste disposal has ceased. According to the Scottish Development Department,

> Of the total of 528 sites containing gas-producing wastes, about 118 (say 25%) may prove to be of prime concern. In such cases, intensive routine monitoring arrangements are likely to be needed quickly and, for many, gas control works may be necessary. At the other end of the scale, perhaps 158 sites fall into a category where only a low level of monitoring may be necessary and where probably no gas control works are required. Between these categories are a further 252 sites carrying an intermediate risk. Assuming that about a third of these (80 - 90 sites) need more or less urgent action, the other two-thirds being towards the lower-risk end of the scale, this means that about 200 should be treated as of immediate concern.

6.69. The scale of the problem and its risks to health, is a major source of concern. Especially when it is known that significant housing and commercial developments have been constructed on completed landfill sites. According to the House of Commons Environment Committee, none of the £5M grant for urgent remedial works of gas producing landfill sites was taken up, in 1989-90. It is hoped that the £33M available for 1990-91 will be taken up.

6.70. Modern landfill sites need to be engineered from the start to contain and control leachate and landfill gas. Landfill should, like any other construction, be designed so the problems will not arise. Such design needs civil engineers, chemists, geologists, hydrogeologists and biologists working together.

Industrial wastes

6.71. The wastes from industrial processes are many and varied. Some may be inert and innocuous, others may be mainly organic such as those from food processing factories, whilst at the other extreme, there are toxic substances such as PCBs and dioxins. These latter can be effectively destroyed by a costly process of carefully controlled high temperature incineration at $1100°$-$1200°C$.

6.72. In the past, dangerous chemicals, such as metal salts and cyanides, have been disposed of on open land, often within the premises of the factory producing them. With time the factory has changed hands and the tip records lost.

6.73. With the pressure to develop urban sites in preference to greenfield sites where possible, many of these areas of contaminated land have come to light, posing problems for the developers and local authorities. It is essential that where disposal operations take place the details should be fully documented and be available when the future development of the site takes place. Civil engineers must be aware of the need to deal with contaminated ground when they design and carry out works on old industrial sites, e.g. gasworks.

Sludges and polluted sediments

6.74. The principal sources of sludges are from sewage and water treatment works, industrial manufacturing processes and from dredging activities in harbours and navigable waterways. Most exhibit high water content, e.g. sewage sludge 95% water, dredged spoil and industrial sludges 75% water. Dewatering of sludges is difficult and expensive. Typical methods include presses, sedimentation ponds, hydrocyclones and centrifuge. Approximately $7Mm^3$ of sewage sludge is disposed of each year in the UK with more that 50% going to the sea, the rest to land. Dredged spoil in the UK amounts to just over $1.5Mm^3$ with over 90% going to sea. Industrial sludges are difficult to quantify, but almost all go to landfill. This is either as co-disposal with other general wastes or in special or toxic waste sites.

6.75. All sludges contain a mixture of inorganic sands and clays, organic materials and chemicals including a range of heavy metals. The mere presence of some chemicals such as cyanide, arsenic and heavy metals such as cadmium, mercury, zinc and lead, make sludges a difficult waste to dispose of.

6.76. The long term disposal of sewage sludge on land would eventually lead to build up of heavy metals in the soil. This would then lead to a build up of these same metals in the food chain. In the short term, sewage sludge spread on land will transfer a variety of parasites which could affect grazing animals. Careful land management is therefore necessary. Disposal of sludges at sea can have an effect on the bottom feeding fauna which can contribute through the food chain to humans.

6.77. The Oslo Convention and the London Dumping Convention together with the EC directives on sea dumping of sludges will significantly reduce the quantity of sludges going to sea and will result in more going to land disposal.

6.78. Research has demonstrated that land disposal of dredged material is economically and environmentally feasible and that dredged material can be recycled into topsoil and brick products with an added value. The Glasgow and West of Scotland Case Study illustrates how River Clyde dredgings have been successfully used as topsoil. Sewage sludges are more difficult to dispose of on land and would require more economical methods for dewatering them, to make land disposal or recycling feasible. A major research initiative is required in this field with the aim of treatment at source. Industrial sludges are the most difficult of the group to dispose of in an environmentally friendly way. Most end up in special waste sites, as a co-disposal with other solid wastes. The long term future for industrial sludge disposal requires detailed appraisal. Methods of identification at source and labelling and identification at point of disposal need improvement. Recovery and recycling of industrial sludges needs fundamental research to bring out a practical cost effective solution. Indeed all sludges need to be treated in a coordinated way to develop a 21st century solution to the disposal of this type of waste, since they represent a great unknown from a public health viewpoint.

Litter

6.79. There is increasing concern among the general public about the problem of litter, particularly in inner city areas like central London. This problem seems to have not been so much caused by big increases in the amount of litter and refuse generated in recent years, as by systematic underfunding and understaffing of municipal refuse collection and street cleansing services over a number of years. In the first half of the 1980s, local authority spending on refuse collection (in England) fell by over 10% after allowing for inflation. Other local authority services, like social services or housing, escaped much more lightly or even grew in the same period. It would seem that one of the key problems with refuse collection is the very low political priority attached to it. This is now changing, and the Environmental Protection Bill contains for the first time an explicit code of practice on litter collection for local authorities. It is hoped that this will be accompanied by greater funding, especially on the capital investment side, of a hitherto Cinderella service.

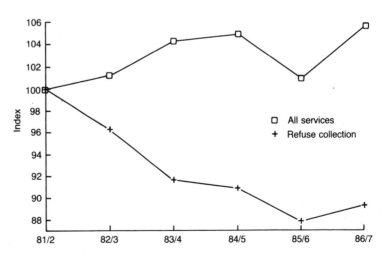

Figure 6.3. Local authority expenditure (rate fund). Constant prices (1981/82 = 100) Source: DoE.

Recycling

6.80. There is a growing awareness that waste is a potentially valuable raw material. Whilst it can perform a useful function in the natural cycle by returning to the earth the elements taken from it, it can be even more valuable if some of the component parts are reclaimed and recycled for re-use. Artificial recycling systems usually consume fossil fuels. To assess the efficiency and justification of such systems, it is necessary to balance the recovery of material resources against the use of energy. Recycling is then socially justified if it is economically viable taking into account all costs, including the cost of manufacturing materials in the absence of recycling. An efficient system of recycling needs the provision of a stable market for the end product. The key to recycling is the creation of demand say for a glass cullet or writing paper made from recycled paper.

6.81. If materials are recovered from waste not only do they conserve natural resources and may provide an income from their sale but the quantity of waste requiring disposal is reduced thus prolonging the life of available landfill sites.

6.82. The principal items from domestic and commercial refuse which can be recycled are paper and board, glass, and ferrous and non-ferrous metal. Where possible, these should be separated at source for separate collection or for depositing at collection points by the householder.

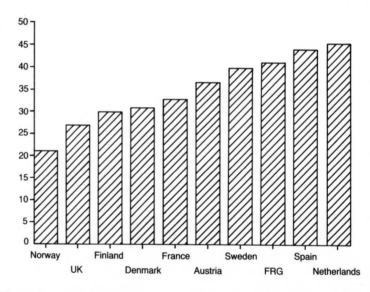

Figure 6.4. Percentage paper and cardboard recycled 1985. Source: OECD Environmental Data 1989.

6.83. Approximately 50% of the material going to landfill at present is waste from the construction industry. In the case of stone and concrete, it is clean fill and can often be used for site roads, etc. Some very effective schemes have been created for reuse of road materials. For example, concrete arising from the reconstruction of the M1 have been stored, crushed and later reused in other roadworks. Bituminous surfacing has been relaid either with the addition of some new material or as dug.

6.84. An inspection of many construction sites demonstrates the need for civil engineering and building firms, like firms in other industries, to have an environmental policy and an hierarchy of waste management. Unnecessary waste, in which much is lost on site and more goes to landfill than is necessary, is an endemic problem. The duty of care to be imposed on all parts of the waste chain will sharpen up the need for the construction industry to take a more responsible attitude to the disposal of its small quantities of chemical waste.

6.85. Where economically viable, the UK should aim to recycle a higher proportion of its products to bring it closer to the rates achieved in other countries. The bar charts (Figures 6.4 and 6.5) reveal that the UK recycles a low proportion of paper and cardboard and glass. However, at present the demand for waste paper in the UK is low and paper is obtained from forests cultivated as a renewable resource. The recycling of glass involves costs of collection and transport costs to bottle banks.

Paper and board

6.86. This forms about one-third of domestic and commercial refuse and is mainly suitable for recycling and manufacturing in low grade paper, board and packaging. The object is to avoid felling large areas of forests, the trees from which are required to meet the paper and board requirements of modern society.

6.87. Whilst there is considerable pressure to conserve the rain forests, it must be realised that these are not the source of wood-pulp for paper manufacture as they consist largely of hardwoods. The trees used for the manufacture of paper are softwoods mainly from the plantations of Scandinavia and North America. The extent to which these are replanted, in accordance with the principles of good forestry, must be taken into account in any assessment of the complete situation which must, of course, include its effect on the economies of the countries affected by any change in policy.

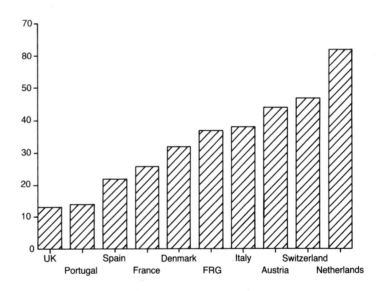

Figure 6.5. Percentage recycled glass 1985. Source: OECD Environmental Data 1989.

Glass

6.88. Silica is the principal ingredient in the manufacture of glass. The principal reason for recycling glass is not to conserve natural resources but to save fuel, as the manufacture of glass from cullet (as broken glass is termed) requires less fuel than glass manufactured from raw materials. A further advantage is that glass on landfill sites does not decompose and remains a minor problem for all time. Even pulverisation only reduces glass to pieces of 25 -40mm in size.

Metals

6.89. Old cars are usually salvaged by specialist firms. Larger items of domestic equipment, such as cookers and refrigerators, are usually the subject of special collections by waste collection authorities and are recycled. An important aspect concerning refrigerators must be the reclamation of CFCs. Smaller items, comprising about 6% of domestic refuse, including the more valuable non-ferrous metals are often hand picked at disposal sites for re-use, but this only reclaims a moderate proportion of available metal. Tins and smaller items, unless collected separately by the householder, are disposed of in landfill, unless the refuse is subject to some form of treatment, such as pulverisation or incineration, when equipment for the magnetic removal of ferrous elements can be incorporated into the processing chain.

Residue

6.90. Residue consists of about 50% organic matter, mainly animal and vegetable food waste, which will decompose with the dust and grit from a reasonable soil. Non-biodegradable plastics and man made fibres, which are about 10% of this residue, do not decompose. Although they are visually undesirable they do not have any significant adverse effect on the soil which is produced.

Methane

6.91. This gas is generated over a long period both during and after the operational life of the landfill site. It is possible, on some sites, to collect this on a commercial basis, usually where there is a great depth of fill. For this to be done efficiently the system for collecting gas must be designed when the original plans for the site are prepared. The gas collected, although mainly methane usually contains about 35% of carbon dioxide, as well as small quantities of other gases such as hydrogen sulphide.

6.92. To impose a gas collection system on an existing site may or may not be an economic proposition but it may be necessary in the interests of safety.

Waste derived fuel (WDF)

6.93. Several experimental plants have been set up to manufacture fuel from the organic elements of domestic and commercial waste and a degree of success has been achieved. These organic elements, mainly paper and board, are manufactured into a low grade fuel either in floc form or as pellets some 15mm in diameter, chopped into 50mm long pieces. This process can reduce the cost of waste disposal to £15 - £20 per tonne which, though generally greater than the cost of landfill, is appreciably less than incineration.

Pulverised fuel ash (PFA)

6.94. It has been mentioned that 10 - 12M tonnes of ash are produced each year from power stations. This ash is mostly a fine material ranging in particle size from 2 - 3mm to dust. Considerable research has been carried out on this material, and as a result, it has achieved a wide usage mainly for two purposes. The first of these is as a fill material for civil engineering projects such as highway embankments. It is very stable, has a minimum of settlement and is easy to use. The second use is for cement replacement, particularly in precast concrete products, where a proportion of the cement is replaced with PFA with satisfactory results in the products and a reduction in production costs. Some is disposed of in the form of artificial hills which can be soiled and seeded.

Oil

6.95. A certain amount of engine oil, mainly from commercial garages, is recycled. In certain areas waste disposal authorities have facilities for accepting small quantities of oil as well, usually from DIY car maintenance enthusiasts. This type of facility must be encouraged and extended as, quite apart from reclaiming oil, it would reduce pollution caused by individuals disposing of their oily waste into the drains and public sewers with the resulting probability of polluting watercourses.

Industrial waste

6.96. The term industrial waste covers a wide variety of substances from chemicals, metal contaminants and sludges to fairly harmless materials which cause no unusual problems in their disposal. Problems, however, can occur when apparently innocuous chemicals are mixed and react with one another to produce hazardous substances, not infrequently in gaseous form.

6.97. In recent years pilot studies have been carried out into the various wastes produced by industry and directories of industrial waste have been compiled. The object of these studies was to make available, to manufacturing firms, information about available industrial wastes so that they could ascertain whether the raw materials they needed were, in fact, being discarded as waste from some other industrial process. So far little success has been achieved.

6.98. Encouragement should, however, be given to firms to reprocess their own waste, where possible, for reuse in their own industrial processes and high disposal costs have gone some way in achieving this end. Firms should be encouraged to develop a waste policy. It starts with getting more from less and develops an hierarchy of waste management objectives which should be

(a)   source reduction
(b)   reuse or composting
(c)   incineration and/or
(d)   landfill

The case study of the East Midlands illustrates the successful recycling of road materials.

The current problem

6.99. It is the responsibility of Government and Local Government to respond to the requirements of the electorate. The electorate has suddenly, in political time scales, become extremely concerned about environmental issues and the legislative machinery is not equipped to cope with sudden change. This, of course, is no bad thing as it gives time for considered judgement of changes in policies and legislation, to the drawing up of new programmes and the reallocation of resources.

6.100. The present problem, in waste disposal, is threefold. Firstly the need to deal with old landfill sites and contaminated land, the legacy of our predecessors. Secondly the need to upgrade existing disposal facilities to reduce any adverse effect they may have on the environment, and thirdly to ensure that landfill sites being planned will operate in conformity to the highest standards.

6.101. The first two items should not be a continuing problem provided that the third item, the planning of new sites receives proper attention.

6.102. The considerable call on existing resources is occurring at a time when Local Government is under attack by Central Government to reduce expenditure leaving little available in budgets for reallocation.

6.103. The Derelict Land Grant has, within limits, been of great assistance in dealing with contaminated land. However, there is still an appreciable amount of money to be found by local authorities out of existing resources.

6.104. Some five years ago the Welsh district councils put together a package of improvements to their waste disposal facilities and operations. At a conference following the presentation of these to the Welsh Office, the Minister of State from the Welsh Office, whilst applauding the initiative, said that the cost was only an additional 3% which would have to be found from district council budgets as no Government assistance would be available. This was hardly encouraging as the district councils had made considerable efforts to achieve higher standards of landfill and were proposing to aim for still higher standards in the future. It did, however, indicate the Governments attitude to this important subject.

The way ahead

6.105. Much has been achieved but there is still a long way to go. The major problems associated with the disposal of waste are well known and research has been, and is being, carried out to find solutions but much remains to be done in continuing current research and also to progress research which has not yet begun or is still in its early stages: pyrolysis, hydrolysis, production of amino acids, dealing with plastics and so on.

6.106. In spite of the increasing awareness of the need to preserve the environment, the awareness is not universal. It is necessary to educate and to inform members of the public and also to encourage them to play their part in recycling and in changes that may be made in the collection and disposal of refuse. Self interest may dictate against change.

6.107. Certain members of the public co-operate in collecting metals, paper and glass for recycling but this is only a small proportion of the waste that could be collected. If there was a sudden increase in the collection of materials for recycling could industry cope? Or would industry cope without some incentive and some guarantee that the flow of materials for recycling would continue? What incentive could be given, tax incentives, or grants for new plant? The former has the advantage of assisting companies that are operating at a profit and therefore, presumably, with reasonable efficiency whilst the latter gives help in the initial stages when it is needed most but does not ensure that the company will operate efficiently or even survive.

6.108. Companies are in business to make a profit and, therefore, fiscal measures which affect that profit may be one of the most effective ways of tackling the problems of unnecessary waste. A tax on waste, if it was levied, could take into account, not only the quantity, but also the potential problems that could be caused due to its composition.

6.109. However important taxes, grants, legislation and similar measures are, it is of vital importance that more research is carried out into solving the problems caused by waste. Fragmented research by individual companies to find solutions to their waste problems is neither efficient nor economic and will therefore not be carried out. Centralised research, funded if necessary by an industrial levy, could be the answer.

6.110. More research needs to be done on methane generation and its collection on a commercial scale. Not only is this economically desirable but it, together with other measure, reduces the possibility of the gas migrating off site and giving rise to potentially explosive conditions. The research must examine more closely the conditions under which methane is generated and how production can be accelerated, not only to improve its commercial viability, but to reduce, if possible, the length of time over which appreciable quantities of the gas are generated, after a site has ceased to be operational

6.111. The development of the production of waste derived fuel could open up further possibilities in view of the reasonably successful results which have been obtained from existing experimental plants.

6.112. A very important area, where little research appears to have been carried out, is the problem of non-biodegradable plastics in landfill. Can the manufacture and use of biodegradable plastics be extended? Is there any possibility of recycling plastic materials and man made fibres? Plastics are, after all, manufactured from fossil fuels, hydrocarbons, which are a finite resource. Recycling may be possible, but recovery except in an industrial situation is probably impracticable.

6.113. The disposal of nuclear waste arises from the decommissioning of the early nuclear power stations. The current method of disposal is to contain the waste in massive sealed concrete bunkers and leave it for decades, or centuries, until its radioactivity drops to levels which are not considered hazardous. Research must be carried out either to harness this residual radioactivity or, if this is impractical, to ascertain methods of decreasing the period during which danger exists and containment is necessary.

6.114. The provisions of the Control of Pollution Act, through site licences, have enabled stricter controls to be imposed and, together with stringent planning conditions go far in reducing the environmental impact of waste disposal on landfill sites. However this is, to some degree, treating the symptoms rather than the disease. The symptoms must be treated as well as the disease.

6.115. The proposals in the Government's Environmental Protection Bill will, if enacted, replace sections of the Control of Pollution Act with more stringent requirements and greater penalties. In addition to the current requirements for waste disposal authorities to prepare waste development plans, the proposals require them to prepare waste recycling plans. Powers are also proposed to vary the conditions of a Site Licence during the operational life of the landfill site.

6.116. Whilst local authorities still remain the prime enforcement bodies, the Pollution Inspectorate, which as the Hazardous Waste Inspectorate had a staff of five and a half some four years ago, will be progressively increased in strength to over ten times that number by the end of 1991.

6.117. Although the bill is similar in principle to the Control of Pollution Act, its proposals are more far reaching, it is more detailed and its controls and penalties for non compliance much more severe.

6.118. There are a number of European Community Directives that relate to waste disposal operations, which have been implemented in the UK by national legislation. Notably, the 1988 Environmental Assessment Regulations (SI 1988 No 1199), which implement the provisions of the EC Directive 85/337/EEC, which came into force in July 1988. These regulations require that before planning permission can be granted for certain types of development, the planning authority must be provided with information on the possible environmental effects of the development in the form of an Environmental Statement.

6.119. The Groundwater Directive effectively rules out the practice of developing landfills on a dilute and attenuate basis. There is therefore a move towards heavily engineered containment sites, with the use of natural or artificial liners (or a combination of both) to provide a barrier to the migration of contaminated leachate into the groundwater system.

Conclusion

6.120. The total quantity of waste produced annually in the UK is about 500M tonnes. Two-thirds of this is agricultural or mineral working waste which is disposed of at or near its point of production. Some of this is used as farm manures or the mineral waste as a fill material.

6.121. The remainder is dealt with mainly by waste disposal authorities or contractors in the private sector. Some materials are recycled or reused PFA, glass, metals and paper but this only accounts for a small proportion of the waste produced.

6.122. The bulk of waste is disposed of on landfill sites at a cost of £2-£3 to £16 per tonne or more, some is incinerated at £20 - £30 per tonne whilst some of the highly toxic chemical wastes are incinerated at a cost of £1,000 per tonne.

6.123. The cost of incineration could be reduced if the heat generated were used in connection with a district heating scheme, where it would be incorporated into the central heating system of a housing estate or a factory. Alternatively it could be utilised for power generation for local use or be fed into the national grid.

6.124. The public conscience is awakening to the need to conserve natural resources and protect the environment. Local authorities, after systematic underfunding of refuse collection in the past, are devoting more resources to waste disposal and Central Government is responding by putting forward legislation to give Government inspectorates and local authorities greater powers of enforcement.

6.125. It is necessary to devote considerable attention and resources to the legacy of the past, such as contaminated land and disused landfill sites, which are still producing leachate and methane.

6.126. New landfill sites must be adequately planned and prepared to avoid polluting the ground, watercourses and aquifers, and the atmosphere. Plans for the ultimate landscaping, and aftercare of sites must be drawn up and financial resources made available for their aftercare until they cease to be a potential environmental hazard.

6.127. Much more research is required into methods of recycling, the production and collection of methane, the development of waste derived fuels as well as dealing with special wastes which arise in comparatively small quantities.

6.128. Finally the public must be educated in the need to conserve natural resources, separate wastes at source where necessary to facilitate recycling, and to play an active rather than a passive role in this aspect of environmental protection.

7.   Coastal problems

Introduction

7.1.   Coastal engineering is a broad area o. chapter relates to those aspects of coastal defen within the context of this report.

7.2.   There is no legal definition of the coastal zone but in oceanographic science the zone is held to extend from the continental shelf up to and including the immediate landward area or coastal terrace. For the purposes of this report the zone will be considered as the foreshore and seaward area within which shifting of sediment can occur, together with areas where leisure activities, construction or industry could affect the regime of the shoreline. Additionally on the landward side, the zone includes areas of land likely to be affected either directly or indirectly by coast erosion or inundation.

7.3.   The environment is influenced by both the characteristics of the coast and the demands made upon it. These include

(a)   beaches and backshore areas which provide an amenity for recreation and tourism
(b)   geological exposures and foreshore and seabed minerals
(c)   coastal flora, fauna and scenery
(d)   access across the foreshore to marinas and other facilities,
(e)   industrial and commercial access to the sea via harbours
(f)   fisheries and fishery based activities
(g)   water extraction for desalination and industrial use
(h)   the construction and maintenance of outfalls and sluices
(i)   residential, public and commercial structures and associated infrastructure
(j)   farmland, pathways and land for recreational activities.

Responsibility for coast defence and the environment

7.4.   Coastal defences in England and Wales are governed by two main Acts of Parliament. These are the Land Drainage Act 1976 and the Coast Protection Act 1949. In general the Land Drainage Act is applied to low areas liable to flooding and the defence works are referred to as sea defences, whereas the Coast Protection Act relates to protection against erosion. The Ministry of Agriculture Fisheries and Food (MAFF) is responsible for administering the Acts in England, and the Secretary of State for Wales is responsible in Wales.

7.5.   In Scotland, the Secretary of State for Scotland is responsible for administering the Land Drainage (Scotland) Act 1958, the Flood Prevention (Scotland) Act 1961 and the Coast Protection Act 1949. In Northern Ireland, the Secretary of State for Northern Ireland is responsible for administering the Drainage Order 1973.

7.6.   Responsibility for the actual sea defences in the coastal zone falls to the various Regions of the National Rivers Authority (NRA), which have taken over the sea defence role from the former water authorities.

7.7.   Coastal defences, defined as coastal protection under the Coast Protection Act, are the responsibility of local authorities such as district councils. There are 88 of these Coast Protection Authorities in England. If one adds the equivalent authorities in Wales, Scotland and Northern Ireland, together with the established ports, then the total number of authorities concerned with the coast total about 240.

POLLUTION

7.8. Apart from those already mentioned there are numerous other bodies such as the Crown Estate Commissioners, Nature Conservancy Council and nationalised industries with interests in the coastal zone.

7.9. There is no single authority responsible for coastal defences in the UK. Although it would be premature to immediately conclude that it would be advantageous to consolidate responsibility under a single authority, there are aspects which would clearly benefit from a national approach. These are referred to in the conclusions.

Environmental aspects

7.10. Some measures, for ensuring that environmental aspects of coastal defence are taken into account, are included in the Acts mentioned above. For instance works carried out under the Coast Protection Act require planning permission. This is not required under the Land Drainage Act, but Statutory Instrument 1217 1988 defines measures likely to have significant effects on the environment.

7.11. Under the Food and Environment Act 1985, licences have to be obtained from MAFF for the construction of coastal works. This Act

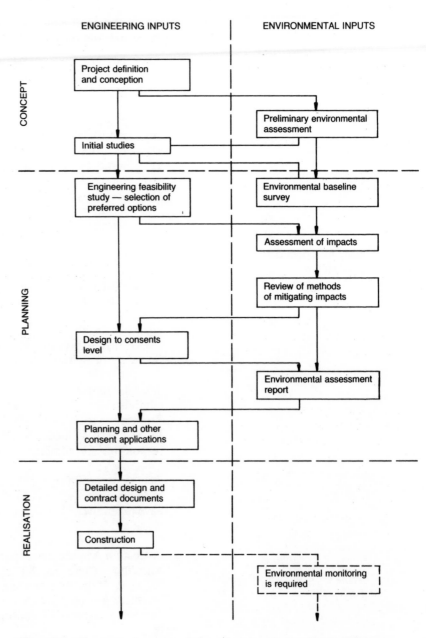

Figure 7.1. Diagrammatic representation of engineering/environmental inputs

is mainly concerned with Fisheries and can include the dumping or disturbance of materials in the sea which might cause pollution.

7.12. The Wildlife and Countryside Act 1981 (updated 1985) is concerned specifically with the environment. In addition there is the Town and Country Planning Act 1971, plus legislation relating to sea fisheries, pollution, dumping at sea, mining, dredging and numerous private Bills and railway Acts affecting the coastal zone.

7.13. Considerable effort is devoted by Government and voluntary bodies on survey and research specifically aimed at wildlife protection and marine conservation. UK expenditure is of the order of £10M per year.

7.14. The Regional Committee structure of the National Rivers Authority (NRA) is also designed to reflect the importance of environmental issues.

7.15. A distillation of some of the statutory obligations relating to conservation is contained in a Government publication entitled 'Conservation Guidelines for Drainage Authorities', the aims of which can be summarised as follows

(a)   to further the conservation and enhancement of natural beauty
(b)   to further the conservation of wildlife and geological features of special interest
(c)   to have regard for the desirability of protecting buildings and items of archaeological and historic interest
(d)   to preserve public rights of access
(e)   to take into account the effect of any proposal on any of the above items.

7.16. Although proposed coast protection works are subject to scrutiny by the planning authority, there are occasions when the latter may make decisions which do not take coastal defence requirements into account. The increasing interest in environmental issues should make authorities more aware of legislative powers which already exist. East Anglian Association has produced two case studies illustrating some of the environmental considerations necessary in the construction of coastal defence schemes.

Coastal defences

7.17. There are approximately 17,000km of coastline round the British Isles of widely varying types. The most vulnerable areas are found on the East and South Coasts of England and, to some extent, in the North West. In some areas erosion of up to 3m per year is not uncommon, and erosion of 20m was experienced over 9 months at Tugnet, River Shey. Other areas are stable and some are accreting.

7.18. In coastal lowlands, ground altitudes are declining as a result of land drainage. In the Fenland, peat wastage from oxidation, blowing and consolidation following dewatering has resulted in a reduction in ground altitudes of up to 3m in 140 years, and ground that was above Ordnance Datum is now 2-3m below Ordnance Datum. A survey is urgently required into the present extent of this expanding area and the impact of long period changes on ground altitudes.

7.19. Traditionally coastal defences fall into two broad categories: hard, e.g. sea walls and revetments, and soft, e.g. dunes and beaches.

7.20. Beaches provide the best means of absorbing wave energy and acting as a natural defence. However, a number of factors including a gradual rise in sea level, urban development in the coastal zone and loss of beach material have meant that the landward extent of many beaches is now insufficient, and they have had to be replenished, backed up or completely replaced by sea walls and revetments.

7.21. Seaside holidays started to become fashionable in the 18th century. Over the next 150 years numerous resorts were developed, many with promenades supported by walls on the seaward side and backed by hotels and houses on the other. A hard line was therefore drawn along the shoreline of many of the present urban areas in the coastal zone. The sea walls constructed at the time were often built too close to the sea, and with changes in sea level and losses of beach material they now form the front line defence.

7.22. In low lying areas, walls and banks have been constructed to prevent the loss of life, property and land due to inundation.

7.23. These defences were not built to modern standards and their repair and replacement now pose a serious problem. Even structures built following the 1953 flood are in some cases nearing the end of their design life.

7.24. It is difficult to state with accuracy the current capital value of the existing coastal defences, but it is probably in excess of £4,000M. The estimated current expenditure on replacement, reconstruction or repair in order to maintain the present level of protection is of the order of £150M per year.

7.25. Table 7.1 gives an indication of the scale of the cost of rising oceanic levels on sea defences.

Table 7.1. Cost of rising oceanic levels on sea defences.

Rise (m)	Range est cost £M	Area (ha)	Commentary
			Dependent on reduction
0.1	0 - 200	6,400	of permitted freeboard
0.3	400 - 900	19,200	
0.5	800 - 2,000	42,000	

Source: Composite from MAFF and Hansard

7.26. The figures only relate to actual defence costs and make no allowance for the affect of erosion and deposition of material as a result of changes to current, tidal flows and coastline alterations. It is not possible to quantify the socio-economic effects the associated disruption will have or to put an estimate on the cost of making good the damage.

Coastal defence planning and management

7.27. Winds, waves, tides, surges and sea and land level changes do not recognise administrative boundaries. The considerable number of authorities responsible for coastal defences has in the past resulted in the implementation of local schemes which did not take account of their potential effect on adjacent areas. Consequently the protection of one area resulted in erosion elsewhere. This tendency is still present, especially when works are carried out as a matter of urgency which is frequently the case.

7.28. There is a greater awareness today of the need to consider coastal planning on a regional basis, taking into account the natural cells within which coastal processes such as sediment supply and transport form a coherent pattern. At the moment, far too little is known about these natural systems and there is no national plan for gathering and analysing them. The Anglian sea defence management study provides an example of what should be done on a national scale. But the lead time related to such investigations is long, and the information is urgently required so that coastal defence solutions are efficient and economical.

7.29. Since the publication by the Institution of Civil Engineers of the Report prepared by the Coastal Engineering Research Panel in February 1985, a number of Authorities responsible for coastal protection and sea defence have formed regional groups. The main common objectives of these groups include the sharing of data and other information, and the discussion of matters of mutual interest in relation to coastal defences and management. At the time of publication ten coastal groups have been established embodying some 72 coastal authorities.

7.30. The formation of these Groups marks a significant step forward, and the Institution's Maritime Engineering Board has provided positive encouragement to their activities. However, it is unlikely that these Regional Groups will be able to carry out investigations of the type initiated by Anglian Region NRA, without substantial Government financial support. There is, however, the possibility of cooperative research which could provide information on common problems at a much reduced cost to individual Authorities. The Institution has made a start on the compilation of a database.

7.31. In the context of the increased emphasis by both Government and the public on environmental matters, efforts are being made to conserve and where possible replenish natural beaches, thus combining defence measures with preservation of the life and character of the coast. Similarly the conservation of dunes and saltings addresses both of these aspects. There are often conflicting requirements, however, and the best compromise solution arises from close consultation between the many and various interests concerned.

7.32. Both in relation to the protection of low value land, nature conservation and the amenities which the coast can offer, it is often difficult, or indeed impossible, to make out a case which can be justified on a cost benefit basis alone. However, attempts are being made at certain locations to quantify the socio-economic effects of rising sea levels. This is because the value of conservation is infrequently capable of quantification in monetary terms. It follows that action in this field is critically dependent upon the attitude of Government to the conditions of Grant Aid.

Marine resources

7.33. The replenishment of depleted beaches with sand or shingle creates a demand on marine resources for these materials from elsewhere.

7.34. The construction industry in general needs vast quantities of aggregate, and the traditional land sources for sand and gravel are, in some cases, reaching the end of economic extraction. Industry is increasingly looking to replacement of the shortfall by the use of minerals from the sea.

7.35. In 1987 nearly 18M tonnes of sand and gravel were extracted from the sea, an increase of 11% on the previous year. In the same year there was an additional requirement of 6M tonnes for beach recharge, coastal protection and landfill.

7.36. Interest is now being shown in alternative aggregates, such as by-products from mining and industrial operations, both for construction and sea defence, but at the moment there is no significant move away from the traditional materials. In the meantime every proposal for offshore extraction should be examined to see that the removal of material does not

(a)   draw down existing beaches
(b)   change the wave refraction pattern and hence the shoreline stability
(c)   prevent onshore movement of sand or shingle
(d)   affect other marine activities such as oyster beds, fish stocks and the food chain.

Sea defence design

7.37. In civil engineering, the forces for which structures or systems have to be designed and the conditions under which they will operate can usually be determined with a reasonable degree of assurance. In coastal engineering these factors are far more difficult to assess.

7.38. As far as the external factors of wind, waves, tides, currents and surges are concerned, only the lunar component of the tide and its associated currents can be predetermined with any accuracy. The others are determined by meteorological factors which vary considerably and, in some cases, unpredictably. Considerable advances have been made in the prediction of wave action in offshore areas in relation, for instance, to the design of drilling rigs and other offshore structures. However, the inshore zone is far more complicated and there is a deficiency of data on the wave climate in the coastal area, and the application of this data to engineering design and the prediction of sediment transport.

7.39. The current debate on the possibility of an increase in global temperatures has identified related increases in global sea level as a major potential problem. This has generated some urgency to understand the processes and their consequences, in order to take account of possible sea level rises in relation to coastal management and engineering design.

The greenhouse effect

7.40. Globally sea levels have been increasing by 0.10m to 0.15m per century since 1870.

7.41. Growth in ocean volume are due to mass increase as a result of the melting of grounded ice and also thermal expansion. It is not clear how this would translate to increases in sea level. It is, however, necessary to anticipate the effects which a rise in sea level would produce.

7.42. Current estimates of sea level rise range between

| 50mm - 410mm | to the year 2030 |
| 70mm - 620mm | to the year 2050 |

Estimates, based on current model results, predict a global rise of approximately 60mm per decade, a rise of 200mm by the year 2030 and of 650mm by the end of the next century. There will be significant regional variations.

7.43. The Report of the Intergovernmental Panel on Climate Change will be discussed at the Second World Climatic Conference in November 1990. The report will address three main aspects:

(a)   the available scientific information on climatic change
(b)   the environmental and socio-economic impacts
(c)   the formulation of response strategies.

Possible effects of sea level rise*

7.44. On the assumption that a significant rise in sea level will take place, the two major effects depend on the influence of climatic change on the frequency and severity of storms, and this is more difficult to assess. However, increased water levels and more severe wave attack will result in overtopping and damage to coast defences.

7.45. Erosion of Britain's coastline is already a serious and growing problem. Sea level rise will threaten assets in the coastal zone, including towns, ports, industry, power stations, agricultural land and amenities.

---

*For further discussion see: Pugh, D.T. (1990). Is there a sea-level problem? Proc. Instn Civ. Engrs, Part 1, 88, 347-366

7.46. Changes in tidal ranges and currents will affect the dispersion of pollutants and the movement of sediments. Discharge points for sea outfalls will thus have to be reviewed.

7.47. The probability of overtopping of existing coastal defences will change as sea level rises. This change may vary between locations depending on particular characteristics. For example, the probability of a given sea level occurring in a 100 years at Newlyn would be reduced to 5 years in 2027 and to less than 1 year by 2087, whereas at Sheerness the corresponding figure would be 60 years and 5 years.

7.48. The significance of these changed environmental statistics for existing and future sea defences will thus vary from place to place. Structures designed for existing conditions will require replacement or development as overtopping becomes increasingly more probable. Groynes will need to be raised and extended landwards together with revetments. Dunes will likewise come under attack.

7.49. As at present, the choice of a design probability will have to be made in the light of the cost of the resulting loss or damage in each particular locality.

7.50. The greatest impact of such a rise in sea level would be on soft coasts protected by sea walls. As the sea rises, erosive processes would become dominant and there would be considerable losses, especially of fine sediments. The slope of the shore would become steeper and each zone narrower. The sea wall would have to withstand increased erosion following the loss of the salt marshes, mudflats and beaches to seawards.

7.51. Failure to provide adequate coastal defences will mean the loss of life, property and land. It is not only areas of low grade marginal land but also areas of high environmental value like the wetlands of the Severn and Thames Estuaries and the peripheral land around the Wash. Areas like the Fens will also be at risk from rising salt levels and destruction of the fresh water habitat. In the UK, some 720,000ha of agricultural land is less than 5m above mean sea level. This includes 57% of all Grade 1 agricultural land (MAFF classification). The most extensive coastal lowland in the UK is the Fenland, and most of this area is Grade 1 agricultural land. It is already well below +5m OD and is at risk; areas immediately east of the A1 are -2m OD and about 45km from the present coast.

7.52. Salt water will penetrate further into estuaries and will also raise the salinity level in groundwater aquifers. Both may influence the abstraction of water for domestic and industrial use. Drainage of low-lying areas of land would also become less effective. Consequences of sea level rise will also have a serious ecological impact on flora and fauna, notably on bird life in estuaries and saltings.

7.53. There are some positive consequences which will mediate the deleterious consequences of sea level rise. Increased erosion of cliffs, sand dunes and marshes will liberate a considerable volume of sediment. There will be an increased need to dredge, and a disruption of outfalls and water intakes for coolant systems. The dilation of tidal flats, saltmarshes and brackishwater lagoons will benefit wildlife whose habitats have contracted due to reclamation.

Possible action

7.54. There will be areas where protection is not vital nor economically justified. For the purposes of Grant Aid, MAFF cannot justify protecting agricultural land due to its low value. Here a strategy for zoning existing land on the assumption that it may have to be abandoned may have to be adopted. Various other options will have to be considered, including raising the existing sea walls, building new walls further inland, and building storm-surge barriers.

7.55. However, the uncertainties in the possible future rise in sea level focus attention on the need to adopt a flexible approach at the present time by making provision in current designs for increasing the height of defences over the life of the structures. Currently, a relative sea level rise of 30cm per century is taken into account in designing sea defences. This is about twice the present trend in sea level rise.

7.56. It is evident that there is no single best policy for adjustment to sea level rise. The implications and possible responses need to be evaluated on a region by region basis, taking into account all aspects of the coastal zone. Clearly, it is vital that decisions are taken early and pursued consistently. This approach will make it less difficult and expensive to adjust to rising sea levels and increased storm frequency.

7.57. There is an urgent need to establish geographical information systems of the coastal lowlands, integrating changing land use data, changing altitudinal data and changing population data with a range of sea level change scenarios. This would provide readily accessible data for government, engineers and planners to assess risk and undertake cost benefit analysis. Accurate time series data is required to resolve the problems of rates of change and predictive models. Actual measurements of extreme water levels on the coast are not taken routinely or incorporated into predictive models.

Conclusions

7.58. The regional coastal groups of local authorities should be supported in their efforts to collect, collate and disseminate local information, and collaborate in the study of problems of mutual interest.

7.59. This will provide the basis for an urgent nationally organised coast defence management study so that local schemes can be based on regional strategic plans. This will enable the best disposition of the extra funds required to take account of the anticipated effects of sea level rise and climate change on existing defences, and on plans for defence in depth or abandonment of some land areas. Worst case scenarios suggest that the annual cost of protecting the coast could rise by a factor of two or threefold, and would have to be maintained for several decades.

7.60. There is need for a national plan for the collection of wave data in areas sensitive to flooding or erosion.

7.61. Planning authorities should consider the designation of 'set back' lines to control development in vulnerable coastal areas.

7.62. The intangible benefits of amenity, recreation and the preservation of the environment must be given a place in cost benefit studies relating to coastal defence.

7.63. A continuing focus for coastal engineering matters in the UK is urgently required, to provide an interface between all those concerned, especially in regard to EC initiatives. This will provide for better dissemination of existing knowledge and recent research activity in the field of coastal engineering.

7.64. There is an urgent need to broaden the base for coastal

8.12. There is little confidence in the local planning system. Outside London only about 20% of England and Wales (by population) is covered by formally adopted local plans. By 1 November 1988 only 57 out of 333 non-metropolitan districts had local plans on deposit or adopted which fully covered their areas. Leaving aside subject plans, some 68 districts have no local plans at all and the remainder frequently have local plans for only a small part of their area. ('The Future of Development Plans' Cm 569). Frequently, developments have been permitted which have either not been in accordance with an adopted local plan or in areas where no plan exists. Refusals by local authorities have been overturned on appeal. The need is urgent for development plans which give full coverage of the land area and which provide sound bases for development control.

8.13. Many district planning authorities have work in hand to extend detailed development plan coverage and it is expected that complete coverage will be achieved in two or three years. This is providing an opportunity for local authorities to tighten control of development. However, it is the Government's intention that these plans will only be 'given considerable weight in dealing with planning applications and appeals' (Cm 569) and 'where there is an up-to-date local plan ... it will carry considerable weight, and the Secretary of State and his Inspectors will be guided by it in dealing with planning appeals' (PPG3). It should be a statutory requirement that no development can be permitted unless it conforms to an adopted plan and that the necessary supporting infrastructure is in place. A system of certification is required whereby no development permission can be given without confirmation from all utility undertakings, transport and other relevant authorities (e.g. education, health, security) that the proposals are acceptable.

8.14. The incorporation into development plans of specific planning standards (e.g. residential densities, plot ratios, site coverage, the physical scale of buildings, parking standards, etc) will do much to assist potential developers as they will be relied upon in the exercise of development control.

8.15. The likely effects of all new development on the environment, including development of the agricultural and leisure industries, must be comprehensively examined in its planning stage. This is achieved by means of an Environmental Impact Assessment (EIA), the requirement for which is the subject of EC Directive 85/337/EEC which was incorporated into planning consent procedures in the UK in 1988. However, the directive specifies that it 'shall apply to the assessment of the environmental effects of those public and private projects which are likely to have significant effects on the environment.' Thus it provides a procedure but lacks statutory enforcement. It should be a statutory requirement that local authorities obtain an EIA for all development at the outline planning stage.

8.16. Environmental assessment ensures that information about the likely environmental effects of a development project is gathered systematically, usually by the developer and his professional adviser, and taken into account by the planning authority when deciding whether to consent to the development. It has been used for many years in other countries and it enables the consequences of a development to be thoroughly analysed before a planning application is made. It is at the outline planning stage that all those involved in the project should ask themselves whether it is necessary to develop at all. Civil engineers have the responsibility to ensure that as much as possible is known about a development proposal, including its likely consequences, so that decisions are based on the best available information. For an EIA to be of value in this process, those to whom environmental statements are submitted must have adequate expertise to make the best use of the information.

Urban design

8.17.   Whatever they do, those involved in the construction industry participate in the creation not only of things but also of places. Places are total environments, that is, the structures and their surrounding areas. Urban communities are places the design of which aims to create interesting and attractive environments in which people can live full and satisfying lives. To achieve this, an urban form is required which is orderly, attractive and coherent and in which each part has its own identity, relates to the main movement networks and integrates with the surrounding environment. The exercise is one involving many professional disciplines working together and which recognises the importance of assessing the implications for the environment of such development. The case studies reveal that Nottinghamshire County Council have carried out substantial improvements in urban areas, and the City of Birmingham has introduced an Urban Renewal Programme.

8.18.   In recent years, there has been much adverse comment on some post-1945 urban development in the UK and it is clear that a wider understanding of the processes involved in the evolution of the design of an urban community is required. A basic requirement of urban design practice is the need to exploit the particular qualities and natural attractions of development sites,   preserving rather than destroying their inherent assets. Adverse effects of development can be diminished; careful attention to the design of construction projects can minimise the use of resources in construction and maintenance and in the functioning of society.

8.19.   In environmental terms, transport is most detrimental in urban areas, because of its proximity to people and its concentration in confined areas. The disposition of buildings dictates traffic flow patterns, and the increase in private car ownership has enabled urban development to disperse very widely. As Sir Colin Buchanan has pointed out, with the arrival of the motor vehicle, town planning was influenced in a way which was the antithesis of those forces which had previously encouraged a compactness of the urban areas, that is, the concentration of development near to railway stations. Transport corridors occupy very large areas of land and planning for them and for other 'hard' engineering infrastructure constructions must aim for economy in land take. Planning principles must include the need to minimise the use of vehicles and expensive road space, and opportunities must be sought for the integration of road, rail, pedestrian and bicycle routes that complement each other. The land used for these routes must be made as humane, harmonious and environmentally friendly as possible.

8.20.   Environmental features which mitigate the visual impact of hard construction and reduce ambient noise levels must be incorporated into all urban development at the design stage, not added later as an emollient. The overall appearance of development and how it is managed and maintained are among the most important determinants of people's satisfaction, and care is required in the choice of construction materials, in design and detailing and in the design of hard and soft landscaping. Open space, visual links and the protection of views are essential elements of urban design which have often been overlooked in the past. Explicit environmental input at the inception stage of any development will significantly influence the design and will enhance the values of the area.

8.21. The quality of urban life has been degraded by the increase in crime and vandalism and the fear of them. The risks must be assessed early in the design stages of all development, and the layout of buildings, roads, footpaths and subways, open spaces, etc. should be designed to help reduce crime.

Buildings and structures

8.22. Buildings and structures, their massing, design and disposition, have a direct visual impact on people. Much criticism has been levelled at some developments, including housing, as being poorly designed and built and therefore subject to rapid deterioration and short life, badly planned in unattractive surroundings, lacking open space and with difficult access to community facilities. In short, the perception of too many developments is that too little consideration has been given to normal human requirements.

8.23. Society is becoming increasingly concerned about damage to the environment and there is a growing antipathy to development generally as is apparent from the numbers of objections made to development proposals. If it is accepted that development, on whatever scale, is inevitable, people need to be reassured that it is possible to develop where the benefits are far greater than the social cost. Part of that social cost is the ugliness and lower quality of the environment perceived by people in past developments.

8.24. While aesthetics are a controversial subject, there is clearly wide acceptance that some developments are visual blights. On the other hand there are excellent civil engineering achievements where the visual impact has been enhanced and where necessary development has been successfully integrated into the natural landscape.

8.25. The incorporation of specific design requirements in planning briefs issued by local planning authorities would help to promote a satisfactory level of environmental quality. It would not be the intention to restrict design innovation and constructive ideas but to specify clear planning and design principles without dictating detailed aspects on implementation. Controls should encourage developers to collectively co-operate closely with the local authority to realise those aspects of

Table 8.1. Construction expenditure as percentage of GDP.

	1980	1983	1984	1985
Switzerland (CH)	14.2	14.2	14.3	-
Germany (FRG)	-	12.5	12.4	-
Canada (CAN)	14.1	12.6	11.7	11.9
France (FR)	-	10.5	9.8	-
Sweden (SWE)	12.1	10.3	9.6	-
Norway (NOR)	10.5	10.3	9.4	9.4
Denmark (DEN)	11.8	9.1	9.3	9.7
Italy (IT)	9.7	9.4	9.1	8.7
USA	9.3	8.3	8.8	8.9
Netherlands (NL)	10.1	7.7	7.5	6.8
Austria (AUS)	6.8	5.9	5.6	-
United Kingdom	5.8	4.4	4.4	4.2
Belgium (BEL)	5.5	3.9	3.3	-

Source: UN Annual Bulletin of Housing & Building Statistics for Europe.

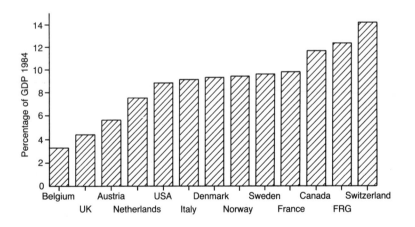

Figure 8.1. Construction expenditure for 1984 (% of GDP). Source: UN Annual Bulletin of Housing & Building Statistics for Europe

urban design that would not be possible for an individual developer to undertake.

8.26. It must be accepted, however, that the environmental quality of housing and of other buildings and structures, be they public or private, can only be at a level which the nation can afford commensurate with the national prosperity. The UK spends less, as a proportion of its GDP, on building and construction than most other western countries, as is illustrated in Figure 8.1 and Table 8.1. The environmental quality of construction has, no doubt, suffered as a result of inadequate investment in that aspect.

8.27. Further, because the UK's per capita GDP is relatively low, the amount spent on construction work relative to population is significantly less than others.

Housing

8.28. The Institution's report on urban regeneration sets out the objectives of housing as being to 'provide a variety of housing stock in attractive surroundings. The accommodation should be desirable, both physically and financially, to a wide spectrum of socio-economic groupings and must be complemented by sufficient community facilities'. The keys to achieving these objectives are

(a) a supply of land in the right areas at a price that will enable dwellings and the supporting infrastructure to be built so that house prices are affordable. 'One of the key functions of the planning system is to provide an adequate and continuous supply of land for housing.... A well planned strategy for housing, which ensures that housing is available where jobs are being created, can make a valuable contribution to the national prosperity and economic growth'. (Planning Policy Guidance: Housing (PPG3) - DoE 1989 (Rev.). It has been questioned whether this can be achieved while still protecting the countryside. While the proportion of land which is developed varies from region to region, 10.7% of the land area of the UK is urbanised (CSO Annual Abstract of Statistics (1981)). Because of the changing social structure, the number of dwellings required relative to population is increasing and this, together with a growing population, means increasing pressure on countryside and wilderness land. Higher residential densities must be accepted if the extent of the urban land area is to be contained and, in order to ensure that the right type of dwelling is built, adequate research into demand is required.

(b) planning and design of residential areas that takes full account of human and natural requirements and values

(c) building design which employs the best design practices and takes account of the environmental implications not only of the use of the various materials available and of their production but of the economy of operations and maintenance of the development

(d) planning and building controls which enforce the best practices in urban and building design processes

(e) management of completed residential developments which ensures well-maintained and attractive public areas

(f) education to improve the public awareness of the benefits of maintaining clean and attractive living conditions.

8.29. National guidance on housing has been given in DoE's Planning Policy Guidance Note PPG3 (1989 (Rev.) and this is welcomed particularly because of its statement that the planning system must 'ensure that established environmental policies are maintained. These policies, to which Government is firmly committed, include the continuing protection of the Green Belts, National Parks and Areas of Outstanding Natural Beauty; the conservation of natural habitats and the protection of the countryside; and the conservation and enhancement of the urban environment and built heritage'.

8.30.   Multi-storey buildings, including housing, pose particular design problems with regard to the living environment. In addition to the need for energy conservation, sound transmission and vibration are problems which, in the past, have not always been tackled, nor has full consideration been given to maintenance. Security in the public areas must be considered at the design stage and buildings must be properly managed; structures and buildings can be designed and built so that vandalism and graffiti are less likely.

8.31.   Housing, commercial and public buildings consume substantial amounts of energy for heating and cooling and commercial and public buildings for their operations. Measures to reduce the demand are discussed elsewhere. Computer-controlled energy management systems are beginning to be incorporated in new and refurbished buildings but it is essential that codes of practice include the requirement for some form of energy management system in all new developments and redevelopments. Leicester City Council's efforts in energy conservation are examples of what can be achieved; a reduction in energy consumption of 15% in 10 years despite an increased number of buildings, a 50% reduction in its energy bill and a reduction in CO_2 emissions of 90,000 tonnes over the same period.

8.32.   The manufacture of most building materials requires the use of non-renewable resources and consumes a great deal of energy and some require the use of environmentally-damaging materials (e.g. chlorofluorocarbons in insulating materials). It is also apparent that there is some resistance to ecologically-friendly building among promoters which needs to be overcome. Research into the development and use of new materials must be directed to the production of those which minimise the depletion of non-renewable resources and to the use of those which are energy-efficient. More attention should be given to the development of timber cultivation and the wider use of its product. Economy in the use of all building materials must have a high priority.

The extractive industries

8.33.   The construction industry requires an adequate supply of the minerals it needs. The extraction of aggregates for this purpose occurs on an extensive scale; the main sources are sand and gravel pits, quarries producing crushed rock, and offshore sand and gravel deposits. In 1986 approximately 202M tonnes of aggregates were used in England and Wales and this is estimated to rise to 226M tonnes by 1995 and 245M tonnes by 2005.

8.34.   The production of the materials necessary for the construction industry often conflicts with the environment. Where gravel pits and quarries are in areas of natural beauty or high population density, they cause noise and visual degradation, and they generate dust and heavy lorry traffic. They are, nevertheless, an indispensable resource, and development must take into account the need to safeguard deposits against proposals which would hinder or prevent extraction. The location of mineral deposits does not always coincide with demand, and extraction may be constrained by the need to protect agricultural land and the natural environment.

8.35.   For these reasons, the supply problems are severe in the South

East and this has highlighted the need for research into sand and gravel resources in areas of high demand. The extension of rail facilities for transporting aggregates, the extension of marine dredging (where it does not damage the marine environment) and research into the possibility of mining aggregates underground are all possibilities for ameliorating environmental impact. The creation of super-quarries enabling the production of relatively low cost aggregates to be transported long distances by sea and rail is already in hand. For example, in the granite intrusions in Scotland, the development at Glensanda, Loch Linnhe, is nearing completion.

8.36. The use of secondary materials such as colliery minestone, clay sand, power station ash and blast furnace slag and the recycling of construction materials such as asphalt and crushed concrete needs encouragement by investment in research. In this connection, the Building Research Establishment has studied the technical suitability of waste materials and industrial byproducts as aggregates. This could reduce the demand for primary aggregates but until transport, quality and other aspects have been properly evaluated, the advantages of this course cannot be determined with any precision. However, without a comprehensive survey of available resources and adequate investment in research, properly managed exploitation of this resource will not be possible.

8.37. Other extractive industries such as mineral soils, open cast coal mining, clay extraction for brick making, mining for ores, etc. also impact on the environment. Planning permission for these activities and construction aggregate extraction, together with the disposal of the bulk waste materials referred to in the previous paragraph, must take into account local impact and transportation requirements. Restoration after completion of an operation is not always practicable, but this is not necessarily disadvantageous. Deposits can be landscaped and planted. Pits can, in some circumstances, be used as leisure water facilities, and elsewhere they can be used for the disposal of waste. It is essential that the arrangements for after use are established at the time planning permission is given so that the full direct financial cost can be evaluated. Planning must be on a consistent basis.

8.38. Extraction, disposal and reuse of materials involves a wide range of public and private entities. Each works in its own market and to its own profit target, and may have little reason to cooperate with others who are affected by or could benefit from its operation. In consequence, national resources may be wasted. An Environmental Protection Agency could bring together the costs and benefits of public and private entities in a way which is not possible in the normal planning process, so that decisions could reflect the overall national interest more fully.

Conclusion

8.39. It is clear that, in the past, there have been significant shortcomings in land use planning, urban design and building control all of which have contributed to a degradation of the environment. But there has been encouraging evidence, over the last year or two, of Government's intention to improve the planning processes and of its commitment to environmental policies. The consultation on and issue of recent national and regional planning guidance has been welcomed, albeit with some reservations on content, and it is stated Government policy to have regional guidance in place in England by the early 1990s.

8.40. Up-to-date county structure plans which, for the time being, will continue to be a key element in the development plan system, together with local plans covering the whole land area should do much to rationalise and facilitate properly controlled development strategies. Their preparation is a challenge to all involved and, if the planning, urban design and development control processes are to be effective aids to the protection of the environment, up-dating of the policy framework provided by the county structure plans and the completion of coverage by local plans are matters of high priority. The requirements therefore are as follows:

(a) Clear guidance on national planning policies. This is disseminated in the form of DoE planning policy guidance notes and circulars and, in many cases, has given clear national guidance. There is, however, some reservation regarding the scope and content of development plans which should include reference to strategic government, institution and community facilities which are major land users. In this context, the need to produce plans which are concise and which concentrate on key land issues is recognised but there should be a strong element of local determination of matters to be included. On the whole, however, the guidance set out in the draft PPG Note: Structure Plans and Regional Planning Guidance (November 1989) should lead to greater confidence in the planning system in general because the present development plan system seems to have been given a more certain future than seemed likely in the recent past.

(b) Comprehensive and unambiguous regional guidance. Since towards the end of 1988, specific strategic guidance has been issued for a number of regions. While this has been generally welcomed as helpful and practical there have been areas where guidance has been felt to have been less than adequate.

(c) County structure plans which include policies on
   (i) housing - to enable sufficient housing to be provided to standards commensurate with anticipated social values
   (ii) conservation in town and country
   (iii) employment - to enable an adequate range of jobs to be available in major industrial, commercial, services, retail and other employment-generating development
   (iv) major facilities in the utilities, public health, medical, education, and security sectors
   (v) the rural economy
   (vi) transport
   (vii) accessibility - to ensure safe and convenient access to a range of social and economic activities and facilities
   (viii) mineral working and the protection of mineral resource
   (ix) tourism, leisure and recreation.

(d) Development plans which are based on comprehensive survey and analysis and which clearly specify development control parameters. In the past, there have been instances where development has been permitted which has not been in accordance with a local plan or where refusal has been overturned on appeal. If development plans are to properly fulfil their control functions, mechanisms must be in place to ensure that
   (i) no development is permitted which does not conform to an adopted development plan
   (ii) the infrastructure necessary to support any proposed development is in place before occupation and use of the development is permitted
   (iii) the implementation of the plans is not prejudiced by political decisions.
The preparation of these plans is mandatory but it is the quality of them and the manner in which they are implemented that will matter if the living environment is to improve.

(e)   Building controls which promote a satisfactory level of environmental quality while not restricting architectural creativity.

8.41.   In any development or redevelopment the civil engineer has a vital role in the design and construction not only of the urban area but of the whole environment - town, countryside and wilderness. Particularly strong is his role in the provision of the basic engineering infrastructure. His involvement in the planning and design processes carries the responsibility to use his skills to protect and enhance the environment, to achieve the maximum benefit at the minimum social cost.

9.   The way ahead

Introduction
The industrial perspective

9.1.   The tremendous advances in the standard of living and economic welfare which most of the world has enjoyed since the Industrial Revolution are the direct fruits of technical progress and innovation, more often than not applied in the manufacturing sectors of the economy. Industries need access to markets, raw materials and sources of power and these needs are provided by the infrastructure of transport, communication, energy etc. networks without which the productive development of society would not be possible. The construction industry, especially its civil engineering sector, provides this infrastructure.

Population growth

9.2.   Industrial development has often been accompanied by population growth, although there is no necessary connection between the two. Developmental pressures for the rest of the century are likely to be strongly influenced by the unprecedented population growth currently occurring in the developing world (e.g. in Africa in 1986 population growth averaged 2.9% p.a.). This is shown in Figure 9.1. Massive industrialisation in the developing world to accommodate this demographic growth will intensify pressures on the world's environment.

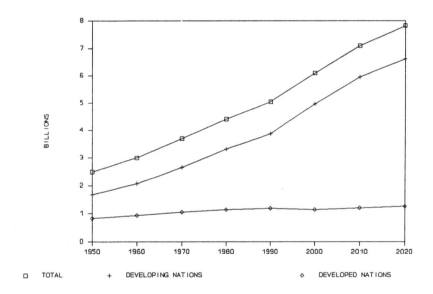

Figure 9.1. World population. Source: Dept of International Economic and Social Affairs, World Population Prospects: Estimates and Projections as assessed in 1984.

Industrial pollution

9.3.   Industrial activities impinge on all of the aspects of pollution of the environment which have been reviewed in this report, for instance:

(a)   Industry is responsible for 33% of world energy consumption. Its demands are therefore the largest cause of the extraction and gaseous emission problems of the energy industry in addition to the similar problems due to its own processes.

(b)   Industry's solid and liquid process wastes are often pernicious and difficult to treat or even contain. They are the bulk of what the UK Control of Pollution Act 1974 identifies as special waste having corrosive, toxic or flammable properties. When they are allowed to intrude into the water cycle they can devastate normal treatment processes and often, effectively, cut the cycle.

(c)   Industry not only contributes its share of controlled waste but also increases the disposal problem by the nature of some of its products, especially when they are non-biodegradable.

(d)   The problem of contaminated land is a legacy from past industrial malpractice. Its treatment, or indeed prevention, is a responsibility that industry has been allowed to avoid.

(e)   Industry is the main user of diesel engined road vehicles, for which no means has yet been discovered (comparable to catalytic converters on petrol engines) to reduce nitrogen oxide emissions.

Management of pollution

9.4.   Operating in a competitive environment, industry is unlikely to be able to respond positively to environmental conservation. Production costs are an important influence on demand and profits in most industries, so managers are continually motivated to minimise the cost of raw material supply, waste disposal etc. Increased market shares will tend to go to producers who can minimise costs rather than minimise damage to the environment. This is an inescapable fact of market economics and is the sole overriding reason why Governments often intervene in the economy to tackle pollution.

9.5.   Thus the management of industry's effect on the environment cannot be undertaken by industry alone. The current rules that provide the framework for their business operations do not motivate in the right direction. Moreover, competition crosses national and continental boundaries and therefore the new regulatory framework to take account of environmental needs must also cross those boundaries. Otherwise the co-operators will be the short term losers, their efforts will be wasted and pollution will continue.

9.6.   The ultimate target must be a worldwide consensus on responsible attitudes to the management of environmental conservation, backed up by international regulations. The natural approach to this seemingly ideal target would be via national and regional developments of standards and procedures, which are seen to be an essential spur to engender responsible attitudes. The initiators of this process must be governments, preferably acting together through geographical groupings such as the EC.

The safety precedent

9.7.   A precedent for this type of development of attitudes to human activity already exists in the field of health and safety at work. National regulations are already well advanced and are in the process of being assimilated in EC directives. The regulations have brought about a much improved awareness of safety responsibilities even though the actual improvements in working practices are happening at a much slower pace. In many industrial organisations the position has long been reached that investment projects which include unsafe practices will be eliminated before their financial viability is even considered. We need to acquire the same attitude to environmental matters.

9.8.   A major cause of the slow rate of improvement in safety practice has been resentment of the perceived interference in individual freedom of action. Such deterrence is less likely to occur in the development of environmental standards as the danger will be seen to be communal rather than individual. Given a strong lead from governments, an international environmental strategy is likely to attract enthusiastic popular support, certainly in the developed areas of the world. How to enlist the support of the less developed areas is an even more taxing problem.

Characteristics of pollution

9.9. Pollution is not a new phenomenon: Pepys's description of the unpleasant atmospheric pollution in the pre-industrial London of the late 17th century, caused by the burning of coal in domestic fires, is a strong reminder of this, as are the smoking chimneys of the typical Victorian milltown. There is ample evidence to suggest that some types of environmental pollution were worse in earlier times than they are now, and this is confirmed by the virtual disappearance of waterborne diseases or choking fog from towns and cities. On the other hand the increased density of the world's population is causing the effects of pollution to become global as well as local. Another key characteristic of environmental pollution is that it is constantly changing, and new forms of pollution spring up. One aspect of this is the way in which apparently successful solutions to the problem are illusory - they simply move it elsewhere. One apparent success of the Clean Air Act was its provision for taller chimneys which spread pollution at a higher level, away from cities but into the atmosphere.

9.10. Two other important characteristics of pollution add further to its complexity. First, the objective effects of polluting substances span a very broad spectrum: at one end there are toxic life-threatening substances (dioxins, ionizing radiation, etc.), whilst at the other end, factors like noise pollution may not actually harm the environment. In between there is an enormous range of substances; and the degree of environmental damage some substances are capable of generating is not known with certainty (the classic example of this is carbon dioxide emissions, the greenhouse effect). Second, the geographical effects of pollutants vary with the nature of the pollution: atmospheric pollution has the ability to affect entire continents, if not the whole globe, but many forms of land pollution are localized.

9.11. All but the most extremely localised and minor forms of pollution cannot be resolved without the intervention of the state. Pollution is a classic example of market failure (where the ability of markets to achieve an efficient distribution of resources in society is compromised). The debate revolves around the form of such intervention.

Objectives

9.12. It is not possible to eliminate environmental pollution. Even if it was possible, it would be prohibitively expensive, and moreover international agreement would not be practicable. The key objective of policy must be to seek an optimal level of pollution; this is the level of pollution where the costs to the environment of a particular activity are balanced by the benefits of the activity to human beings as a whole. This is consistent with the concept of sustainable development. This term is incapable of strict definition but is usually taken to mean that the mutual interdependence of the economy with the environment implies the need for development, (which has hitherto conventionally been defined in economic terms) to incorporate environmental constraints, and pay heed to the interests of future generations. Sustainable development implies that pollution is the product of inappropriate patterns of economic growth, rather than being caused by economic growth itself. The corollary is that programmes to deal with environmental damage do not necessarily have to impede economic growth, and past environmental programmes in most OECD countries have had relatively little impact on growth. As environmental standards become more demanding, the future effects on growth may be more severe, but this should not be used as an argument to prevent a programme of environmental enhancement in view of the high cost of being wrong. Furthermore, the benefits of such a programme are not always included in conventional means of economic growth.

9.13. In relevant timescales, development is short term, whereas the

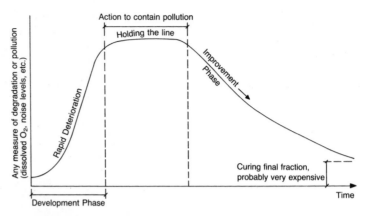

Figure 9.2. Environmental degradation for specific pollution problems. Arguably the development phase is essential to generate the wealth to allow there to be concern about pollution and the environment. Only transfer of wealth from rich nations to poorer ones could break this cycle

environment is long term. Policy to achieve sustainable development must reflect four key considerations:*

(a) The global environment must be treated as one.
(b) The environment must be positively valued in economic decision making.
(c) There must be concern for the wellbeing of future generations ('intergenerational equity').
(d) Concern must also be shown towards the less advantaged ('intragenerational equity').

9.14. The need to regard the world's environment as a single entity derives from the pervasive nature and effects of pollution, particularly atmospheric emissions. Even though the world is riven by nationalism and divided into nation-states, there is only one ecosystem and one planet. This means that countries must modify familiar concepts of economic sovereignty. There are already well-established precedents for this in the economic sphere: most countries have agreed by treaty, for example, to permit the IMF rights of surveillance over their economy. The global challenges of environmental pollution mean that countries will have to allow international agencies to supervise the quality of economic growth in addition to the quantitative surveillance which is already undertaken. What is also certain is that pollution, global, national or local, requires a coordinated response by Government.

9.15. This goal can only be progressed through supranational agencies, like those of the UN, and regional bodies, like the EC, OAS, ASEAN, Comecon etc.) The Brundlandt Report 'Our Common Future' has identified the main needs as follows

(a) Agreement on environmentally acceptable standards of pollution, including the need for regulations to control the impact of industrial activities across national boundaries
(b) Integration of environmental concerns into international trade and development agreements by changes to the mandate of regulatory and advisory bodies and programmes (GATT, CAP , Comecon, OECD, IBRD, IMF etc.). Criteria for development assistance of international development agencies must in future

* Professor D. Pearce and others, Sustainable Development: The implications of sustainable development for resource accounting, project appraisal and integrative environmental policy. (London Environmental Economics Centre 1989)

refer to environmental criteria. International trade agreements must be agreed controlling trade in environmentally pollutive substances and international agencies must be responsible for the environmental surveillance of countries which are members of trade and aid programmes

(c) Alterations to development patterns to encourage lower dependence on scarce resources (energy and other natural resources)

(d) Increased aid flows into environmentally beneficial developments.

Valuing the environment

9.16. The reason most pollution damage occurs is because the environment is treated as 'free'. The citizen is not obliged to pay for the privilege of enjoying pleasant views, drinking water or breathing unpolluted air. Most people, however, would rather pay to continue to consume these rather than forego them and therefore attach a positive value to environmental benefits. Governments need to reflect this concern by altering their own investment criteria to take explicit account of environmental costs and benefits; within the EC, and indeed elsewhere, the major instrument available is Environmental Impact Assessment (EIA).

Environmental Impact Assessment

9.17. This is essentially a process for identifying the probable consequences for the biophysical environment and human health and welfare of projects and policies. In the US, the National Environment Policy Act (1969) made such assessments mandatory for certain projects, a step which the EC followed in July 1985 with publication of a Directive (Annex 9.A) incorporated into UK law in 1988.

9.18. Projects eligible for EIA are usually identified through a screening process: in some cases lists of projects which should be subject to EIA are drawn up (Annex 9.A). In practice, however, the evolution of EIA methods in the UK and the EC has inevitably been shaped by political pressures and compromises which have weakened its effectiveness.

(a) Certain issues cannot be addressed efficiently at the project level and the effectiveness of EIA could be enhanced if policies and programmes as well as individual projects could be assessed. When the 1985 EC Directive was being originally formulated, it was suggested that its scope should extend to this. However, political opposition from member states prevented this proposal from coming to fruition.

(b) Projects 'adopted by a specific act of legislation' are exempted from the requirement for EIA. Thus the Channel Tunnel, the most important civil engineering project this century, which was passed through Parliament using the hybrid bill procedure, fell outside the scope of the EC Directive.

(c) One Government department (the Ministry of Agriculture) has refused to implement all of the provisions of the EC Directive which apply.

9.19. The UK Government's approach to the implementation of the EC Directive on EIA, in general has been characterised by a strategy of containment, so that the net impact on environmental protection might be relatively modest. What is lacking is a necessary commitment to the very goals of the EC directive - anticipatory environmental policy. In the opinion of Pearce 'From UK experience, it is clear that the national perception of priorities concerning development and the environment, is likely to be the major factor in applying EIA, rather than the existence of an EIA directive. Furthermore, those who look to EIA as a means of balancing the legitimate, but competing, demands of development and the environment, particularly when government has a pre-stated interest in the outcome, have been afforded little encouragement by the provisions of the EC Directive'.

9.20. In addition, policy instruments should be modified, principally by changes to taxation but also by other forms of public expenditure and regulation, to oblige polluters to behave as though the environment does have a price tag attached to it (this is dealt with below).

9.21. Furthermore, purpose-built agencies and organisations, separate from Government, may be required to unify national policy on the environment. At present, the Secretary of State for the Environment has primary responsibility for the co-ordination of environmental legislation and policy in the UK as a whole and its implementation in England (in Wales and Scotland this is the function of the territorial departments). Within DoE there is a Minister of State specifically delegated with environmental protection. The Central Directorate of Environmental Protection in DoE is the management resource for the overall monitoring, assessment and co-ordination of the British environment and policy.

9.22. Within the DoE executive Directorates are charged with the implementation of environmental policy; these include

(a) Her Majesty's Inspectorate of Pollution (embracing air, water, and waste pollution - mostly from industrial sources etc.)
(b) Directorate of Air, Noise and Wastes
(c) Water Directorate

Other government pollution control responsibilities are divided amongst other Ministries. Thus the DTI retains responsibility for the control of marine pollution and aircraft noise, the Ministry of Agriculture for the control of agricultural chemicals like pesticides and dumping at sea, the Department of Transport for imposing curbs on vehicle emissions, and the Health and Safety Executive (part of the Department of Employment) for environmental problems related to occupational health and safety.

9.23. In the US, the enforcement of Federal environmental policy is the task of the Environmental Protection Agency (EPA), a body of the Federal Government. Despite its extensive powers, the EPA has not been especially effective in the US, partly because its approach has been unnecessarily legalistic and adversarial. On the other hand, the creation of an EPA for the UK would, by removing the enforcement of environmental policy from a main Government department to a separate agency, enable more effective environmental policing and co-ordination of the policies of Government - a key argument in its favour. Its status would be much reinforced by an independent, arms length relationship vis-a-vis Government.

9.24. In order to make action effective in dealing with the containment of pollution the size and scope of the problem needs to be clearly defined. This is not simply a matter of education at Government level. Present emotional attitudes produce a fog in which the reality is obscured. Without much greater certainty as to the cause and effect, which must involve research, the possibility of solving problems is quite remote.

Research

9.25. More widespread and intensive research is needed in the following areas

(a) To establish the facts about environmental pollution. This is vital

with better conservation measures. Consideration should therefore be given to the following measures:

(a)   Regular audits of the environmental impact of company activities need to be undertaken, perhaps every five years and companies should be obliged to publish them. Action plans should be drawn up to indicate how environmental goals will be attained (the existing interest of the DoE in environmental auditing of companies is supported).

(b)   The same audits should apply to multinational companies with investments in less developed countries to ensure that their activities there comply with good environmental practice (though the problems of implementation would be great). This would discourage multinationals from evading tight pollution controls in their host country by relocating in countries with less stringent standards

(c)   The teaching of environmental concerns in business schools and on accountancy courses should be encouraged

(d)   Expertise in the rational use of energy needs to be developed as a speciality - engineers have a major role to play in the propagation of alternative sources.

Planning controls

9.37. The framework of planning controls is the major way in which Government can impose its requirements on developers. Hence, planning controls and regulations need to be altered to incorporate environmental concerns. In particular, the following changes are needed:

(a)   The transport needs of different types of development is a critically important variable in evaluating overall environmental effects; hence, there needs to be better integration of land use planning with transport

(b)   The scope of local authority plans needs to be extended to give full coverage of relevant land areas

(c)   The ability of planning authorities to enforce compliance with local plans needs to be strengthened

(e)   Planning and building controls need to be able to enforce best practices in urban building/design processes.

(f)   Central Government must give local authorities clear guidance on national planning priorities. Regional planning guidance should also be of a high quality.

Fiscal incentives

9.38. Taxation provides government with a powerful and efficient technique for dealing with the many challenges of environmental pollution; moreover, taxation as a means of intervention is incentive-based. The main alternative is administrative regulation. With this system polluters do not have an incentive to reduce pollution to below the standards laid down by Government (despite this regulation is by far the most common method governments use for dealing with pollution). Another way of tackling pollution with incentives would be to offer tax allowances to encourage investment in non-polluting technology. The main disadvantage of subsidies is that they contravene the Polluter Pays principle.

9.39. For maximum efficiency, pollution taxes should be 'fine-tuned' to penalize polluters for the external costs of their activities: the tax rate would thus be variable more or less in line with the content and quantity of the pollution. In practice because such taxes would be costly to enforce (the monitoring of emissions would have to be intensive) they are perhaps suitable for only a few industries with large-scale integrated operations and well-defined pollution characteristics (e.g. chemicals, iron and steel, power generation etc.). Alternatively taxes could be imposed on inputs (like primary resources). This would be easier to administer in practice as evasion would be more difficult and monitoring simpler.

Marketable pollution permits

9.40. Attention in the past few years has focused on the use of marketable pollution permits to control pollution. With this technique, governments broadly establish a quota defining the amount of pollution permissible, by reference to a level which the environment can absorb. Permits are allocated to producers which are effectively licences allowing them to pollute up to a certain level. Permits can be traded in an open market so 'clean' producers can make money by selling their permits to 'dirty' ones (and vice versa). Using this technique governments can establish the amount of pollution they are willing to put up with and, by reducing permits over time, can lower pollution or even eliminate it. This is a more efficient way of pollution control than a straight tax on emissions or inputs, because companies are more aware than external regulators what the relative cost of pollution is, compared with non-pollution. Companies can make money by selling their unnecessary permits, which is a stronger incentive than a simple tax-based system. However, this is suitable for only a few industries with large integrated plant to facilitate monitoring.

9.41. Thus Government should consider the introduction of marketable pollution permits in the iron and steel and electrical generation industries to discourage atmospheric pollution, principally carbon dioxide and acid rain. Companies operating in these industries would thus be allocated with marketable carbon and sulphur permits (perhaps extended to include nitrogen oxides as well); bearing in mind that short-run costs of effective emission control in these industries would be very big, such a programme would have to be phased in slowly over a number of years to minimise adjustment costs for the economy.

Energy tax

9.42. Households and transport users account for about half of the UK's energy consumption. The application of emission taxes in these sectors would be impractical, so input taxes on energy should be considered (again, adjustment costs should be minimised by phasing in these taxes over a long period);

(a)   the imposition of VAT on domestic fuel bills in the UK (UK is the only country which does not do this).
(b)   increase in duty for motor vehicle fuel (both petrol and diesel), the real price of petrol in the UK is currently very low by historic standards; to raise prices to their 1975 peak would need an increase in duty of about 55%
(c)   the introduction of road pricing for motor vehicles in urban areas.

9.43. These tax changes in private transport would eventually cause a steep progressive rise in its relative price and should be accompanied by changes in public investment criteria to facilitate investment in public transport, which is roughly 10 times as energy efficient as private motoring. Present investment frameworks assess road and public transport infrastructure in different ways inducing a permanent bias against rail transport. This perpetuates a preference for long haul freight transport by diesel powered road vehicles, whose emissions are environmentally damaging in contrast to electrically powered trains. Future public investment criteria should be modified to take account of cost-benefit criteria, in particular taking explicit account of environmental factors.

9.44. Outside the energy sector, where dealing with harmful emissions is a priority, the scope for using taxation as an instrument of policy offers less scope except

(a)   to encourage recycling of selected natural resources to discourage excessive use
(b)   to levy bigger charges for all toxic waste effluent from industry in line with the Polluter Pays principle.

Conclusion

9.45. In order to tackle the problem of pollution this report has dealt sequentially and arbitrarily with areas in which it occurs. This division into chapters may have the appearance of suggesting that the problems are different and separable, and the fact that they are dealt with by separate organizations lends support to this.   This is an illusion. There are few aspects of pollution which are not connected. If global warming causes rising sea levels, or there are rising groundwater levels, there will be an immediate effect on landfill sites. This link between coastal defence and waste disposal, that is, between water and its toxicity in relation to waste disposal, is not the responsibility of any one body. Global warming also brings into consideration the interaction of transport and energy policy.   The many and various organisations involved in responding to pollution which are described in this report, indicate the many and various ways in which pollution can originate. It also makes clear, directly and by implication, that the overwhelming need is for coordination of the measures to contain it.

9.46. There is a demonstrable and pressing need for Government to respond by taking as broad a view as possible. This might take the form of maximising inter-departmental coordination. But Government is organised on departmental rather than functional grounds, and it is extremely difficult in practice to achieve the high degree of integration needed in Government policy, to cope in the many crucial situations where aspects of pollution overlap.   There is also the 'poacher and gamekeeper' problem in that Government policy on, say, energy and transport obviously is capable of exerting a major impact on the environment, but there are conflicts of interest which might affect the willingness of individual departments to implement environmental policy initiatives.   There must also be some doubt as to whether Government as a whole can sufficiently detach itself from interest groups, electoral and political considerations, not to mention the needs of public finance and taxation, to take the synoptic, long term view which environmental problems demand. An agency separate from Government would not have these problems and if it was armed with sufficient powers would be able to achieve the high degree of integration required, together with an across the board view. These are powerful arguments in favour of an Environmental Protection Agency to which Government must give serious consideration.

POLLUTION

ANNEX 9.A.

Official Journal of the European Communities

COUNCIL DIRECTIVE
of 27 June 1985
on the assessment of the effects of certain public and private projects on the
environment

(85/337/EEC)

THE COUNCIL OF THE EUROPEAN
COMMUNITIES,

Having regard to the Treaty establishing the European
Economic Community, and in particular Articles 100
and 235 thereof,

Having regard to the proposal from the Commission [1],

Having regard to the opinion of the European
Parliament[2],

Having regard to the opinion of the Economic and
Social Committee[3],

Whereas the 1973[4] and 1977[5] action programmes
of the European Communities on the environment, as
well as the 1983[6] action programme, the main
outlines of which have been approved by the Council
of the European Communities and the representatives
of the Governments of the Member States, stress that
the best environmental policy consists in preventing
the creation of pollution or nuisances at source, rather
than subsequently trying to counteract their effects;
whereas they affirm the need to take effects on the
environment into account at the earliest possible stage
in all the technical planning and decision-making
processes; whereas to that end, they provide for the
implementation of procedures to evaluate such effects;

Whereas the disparities between the laws in force in
the various Member States with regard to the assessment of the environmental effects of public and
private projects may create unfavourable competitive
conditions and thereby directly affect the functioning of
the common market; whereas, therefore, it is necessary to approximate national laws in this field pursuant
to Article 100 of the Treaty;

Whereas, in addition, it is necessary to achieve one of
the Community's objectives in the sphere of the
protection of the environment and the quality of life;

[1] OJ No C 169, 9.7.1980, p.14.
[2] OJ No C 66, 15.3.1982, p.89.
[3] OJ No C 185, 27.7.1981, p.8.
[4] OJ No C 112, 20.12.1973, p.1.
[5] OJ No C 139, 13.6.1977, p.1.
[6] OJ No C 46, 17.2.1983, p.1.

Whereas, since the treaty has not provided the powers
required for this end, recourse should be had to Article
235 of the Treaty;

Whereas general principles for the assessment of environmental effects should be introduced with a view to
supplementing and coordinating development consent
procedures governing public and private projects likely
to have a major effect on the environment;

Whereas development consent for public and private
projects which are likely to have significant effects on
the environment should be granted only after prior
assessment of the likely significant environmental
effects of these projects has been carried out; whereas
this assessment must be conducted on the basis of the
appropriate information supplied by the developer,
which may be supplemented by the authorities and by
the people who may be concerned by the project in
question;

Whereas the principles of the assessment of environmental effects should be harmonized, in particular
with reference to the projects which should be subject
to assessment, the main obligations of the developers
and the content of the assessment;

Whereas projects belonging to certain types have
significant effects on the environment and these
projects must as a rule be subject to systematic assessment;

Whereas projects of other types may not have significant effects on the environment in every case and
whereas these projects should be assessed where the
Member States consider that their characteristics so
require;

Whereas, for projects which are subject to assessment,
a certain minimal amount of information must be
supplied, concerning the project and its effects;

Whereas the effects of a project on the environment
must be assessed in order to take account of concerns
to protect human health, to contribute by means of a
better environment to the quality of life, to ensure
maintenance of the diversity of species and to maintain
the reproductive capacity of the ecosystem as a basic
resource for life;

No L 175/41   Official Journal of the European Communities   5.7.85

Whereas, however, this Directive should not be applied to projects the details of which are adopted by a specific act of national legislation, since the objectives of this Directive, including that of supplying information, are achieved through the legislative process;

Whereas; furthermore, it may be appropriate in exceptional cases to exempt a specific project from the assessment procedures laid down by this Directive, subject to appropriate information being supplied to the Commission,

HAS ADOPTED THIS DIRECTIVE:

Article 1

1. This Directive shall apply to the assessment of the environmental effects of those public and private projects which are likely to have significant effects on the environment.

2. For the purposes of this Directive:

'project' means:

-- the execution of construction works or of other installations or schemes;
-- other interventions in the natural surroundings and landscape including those involving the extraction of mineral resources;

'developer' means:

the applicant for authorization for a private project or the public authority which initiates a project;

'development consent' means:

the decision of the competent authority or authorities which entitles the developer to proceed with the project.

3. The competent authority or authorities shall be that or those which the Member States designate as responsible for performing the duties arising from this Directive.

4. Projects serving national defence purposes are not covered by this Directive.

5. This Directive shall not apply to projects the details of which are adopted by a specific act of national legislation, since the objectives of this Directive, including that of supplying information, are achieved through the legislative process.

Article 2

1. Member states shall adopt all measures necessary to ensure that, before consent is given, projects likely to have significant effects on the environment by virtue *inter alia*, of their nature, size or location are made subject to an assessment with regard to their effects.

These projects are defined in Article 4.

2. The environmental impact assessment may be integrated into the existing procedures for consent to projects in the Member States, or, failing this, into other procedures or into procedures to be established to comply with the aims of this Directive.

3. Member States may, in exceptional cases, exempt a specific project in whole or in part form the provisions laid down in this Directive.

In this event, the Member States shall:

(a) consider whether another form of assessment would be appropriate and whether the information thus collected should be made available to the public;
(b) make available to the public concerned the information relating to the exemption and the reasons for granting it;
(c) inform the Commission, prior to granting consent, of the reasons justifying the exemption granted, and provide it with the information made available, where appropriate, to their own nationals.

The Commission shall immediately forward the documents received to the other Member States.

The Commission shall report annually to the Council on the application of this paragraph.

Article 3

The environmental impact assessment will identify, describe and assess in the appropriate manner, in the light of each individual case and in accordance with the Articles 4 to 11, the direct and indirect effects of a project on the following factors:

-- human beings, fauna and flora,
-- soil, water, air, climate and the landscape,
-- the inter-action between the factors mentioned in the first and second indents,
-- material assets and the cultural heritage.

Article 4

1. Subject to Article 2 (3), projects of the classes listed in Annex I shall be made subject to an assessment in accordance with Articles 5 to 10.

2. Projects of the classes listed in Annex II shall be made subject to an assessment, in accordance with Articles 5 to 10, where Member States consider that their characteristics so require.

To this end Member states may *inter alia* specify certain types of projects as being subject to an assessment or may establish the criteria and/or thresholds necessary to determine which of the projects of the classes listed in Annex II are to be subject to an assessment in accordance with Articles 5 to 10.

Article 5

1. In case of projects which, pursuant to Article 4, must be subjected to an environmental impact assessment in accordance with Articles 5 to 10, Member States shall adopt the necessary measures to ensure that the developer supplies in an appropriate form the information specified in Annex III inasmuch as:

(a) the Member States consider that the information is relevant to a given stage of the consent procedure and to the specific characteristics of a particular project or type of project and of the environmental features likely to be affected;

(b) the Member States consider that a developer may reasonably be required to compile this information having regard *inter alia* to current knowledge and methods of assessment.

2. The information to be provided by the developer in accordance with paragraph 1 shall include at least:

-- a description of the project comprising information on the site, design and size of the project.

-- a description of the measures envisaged in order to avoid, reduce and, if possible, remedy significant adverse effects,

-- the data required to identify and assess the main effects which the project is likely to have on the environment,

-- a non-technical summary of the information mentioned in indents 1 to 3.

3. Where they consider it necessary, Member States shall ensure that any authorities with relevant information in their possession make this information available to the developer.

Article 6

1. Member States shall take the measures necessary to ensure that the authorities likely to be concerned by the project by reason of their specific environmental responsibilities are given an opportunity to express their opinion on the request for development consent. Member States shall designate the authorities to be consulted for this purpose in general terms or in each case when the request for consent is made. The information gathered pursuant to Article 5 shall be forwarded to these authorities. Detailed arrangements for consultation shall be laid down by the Member States.

2. Member States shall ensure that:

-- any request for development consent and any information gathered pursuant to Article 5 are made available to the public.

-- the public concerned is given the opportunity to express an opinion before the project is initiated.

3. The detailed arrangements for such information and consultation shall be determined by the Member States, which may in particular, depending on the particular characteristics of the projects or sites concerned:

-- determine the public concerned,

-- specify the places where the information can be consulted,

-- specify the way in which the public may be informed, for example by bill-posting within a certain radius, publication in local newspapers, organization of exhibitions with plans, drawings, tables, graphs, models,

-- determine the manner in which the public is to be consulted, for example, by written submissions, by public enquiry,

-- fix appropriate time limits for the various stages of the procedure in order to ensure that a decision is taken within a reasonable period.

Article 7

Where a Member State is aware that a project is likely to have significant effects on the environment in another Member State or where a Member State likely to be significantly affected so requests, the Member State in whose territory the project is intended to be carried out shall forward the information gathered pursuant to Article 5 to the other Member State at the same time as it makes it available to its own nationals. Such information shall serve as a basis for any consultations necessary in the framework of the bilateral relations between two Member States on a reciprocal and equivalent basis.

Article 8

Information gathered pursuant to Articles 5, 6 and 7 must be taken into consideration in the development consent procedure.

Article 9

When a decision has been taken, the competent authority or authorities shall inform the public concerned of:

-- the content of the decision and any conditions attached thereto,

-- the reasons and considerations on which the decision is based where the Member States' legislation so provides.

No L 175/43   Official Journal of the European Communities   5.7.85

The detailed arrangements for such information shall be determined by the Member States.

If another Member State has been informed pursuant to Article 7, it will also be informed of the decision in question.

Article 10

The provisions of this Directive shall not affect the obligation on the competent authorities to respect the limitations imposed by national regulations and administrative provisions and accepted legal practices with regard to industrial and commercial secrecy and the safeguarding of the public interest.

Where Article 7 applies, the transmission of information to another Member State and the reception of information by another Member State shall be subject to the limitations in force in the Member State in which the project is proposed.

Article 11

1. The Member States and the commissions shall exchange information on the experience gained in applying this Directive.

2. In particular, Member States shall inform the Commission of any criteria and/or thresholds adopted for the selection of the projects in question, in accordance with Article 4 (2), or of the types of projects concerned which, pursuant to Article 4 (2), are subject to assessment in accordance with Articles 5 to 10.

3. Five years after notification of this Directive, the Commission shall send the European Parliament and the Council a report on its application and effective-

ness. The report shall be based on the aforementioned exchange of information.

4. On the basis of this exchange of information, the Commission shall submit to the council additional proposals, should this be necessary, with a view to this Directive's being applied in a sufficiently coordinated manner.

Article 12

1. Member States shall take the measures necessary to comply with this Directive within three years of its notification(1).

2. Member States shall communicate to the Commission the texts of the provisions of national law which they adopt in the field covered by this Directive.

Article 13

The provisions of this Directive shall not affect the right of Member States to lay down stricter rules regarding scope and procedure when assessing environmental effects.

Article 14

This Directive is addressed to the Member States.

Done at Luxembourg, 27 June 1985.

For the Council

The President

A. BIONDI

---

(1)This Directive was notified to the Member States on 3 July 1985.

ANNEX I

PROJECTS SUBJECT TO ARTICLE 4 (1)

1. Crude-oil refineries (excluding undertakings manufacturing only lubricants from crude oil) and installations for the gasification and liquefaction of 500 tonnes or more of coal or bituminous shale per day.

2. Thermal power stations and other combustion installations with a heat output of 300 megawatts or more and nuclear power stations and other nuclear reactors (except research installations for the production and conversion of fissionable and fertile materials, whose maximum power does not exceed 1 kilowatt continuous thermal load).

3. Installations solely designed for the permanent storage or final disposal of radioactive waste.

4. Integrated works for the initial melting of cast-iron and steel.

5. Installations for the extraction of asbestos and for the processing and transformation of asbestos and products containing asbestos: for asbestos-cement products, with an annual production of more than 20,000 tonnes of finished products, for friction material, with an annual production of more than 50 tonnes of finished products, and for other uses of asbestos, utilization of more than 200 tonnes per year.

6. Integrated chemical installations.

7. Construction of motorways, express roads[1] and lines for long-distance railway traffic and of airports[2] with a basic runway length of 2,100 m or more.

8. Trading ports and also inland waterways and ports for inland-waterway traffic which permit the passage of vessels of over 1,350 tonnes.

9. Waste-disposal installations for the incineration, chemical treatment or land fill of toxic and dangerous wastes.

---

[1] For the purposes of the Directive 'express road' means a road which complies with the definition in the European Agreement on main international traffic arteries of 15 November 1975.
[2] For the purposes of this Directive, 'airport' means airports which comply with the definition in the 1944 Chicago Convention setting up the International Civil Aviation Organization.

ANNEX II

PROJECTS SUBJECT TO ARTICLE 4 (2)

1. **Agriculture**

   (a) Projects for the restructuring of rural land holdings.
   (b) Projects for the use of uncultivated land or semi-natural areas for intensive agricultural purposes.
   (c) Water-management projects for agriculture.
   (d) Initial afforestation where this may lead to adverse ecological changes and land reclamation for the purposes of conversion to another type of land use.
   (e) Poultry-rearing installations.
   (f) Pig-rearing installations.
   (g) Salmon breeding.
   (h) Reclamation of land from the sea.

2. **Extractive industry**

   (a) Extraction of peat.
   (b) Deep drillings with the exception of drillings for investigating the stability of the soil and in particular:
       -- geothermal drilling,
       -- drilling for the storage of nuclear waste material,
       -- drilling for water supplies.
   (c) Extraction of minerals other than metalliferous and energy-producing minerals, such as marble, sand, gravel, shale, salt, phosphates and potash.
   (d) Extraction of coal and lignite by underground mining.
   (e) Extraction of coal and lignite by open-cast mining.
   (f) Extraction of petroleum.
   (g) Extraction of natural gas.
   (h) Extraction of ores.
   (i) Extraction of bituminous shale.
   (j) Extraction of minerals other than metalliferous and energy-producing minerals by open-cast mining.
   (k) Surface industrial installations for the extraction of coal, petroleum, natural gas and ores, as well as bituminous shale.
   (l) Coke oven (dry coal distillation).
   (m) Installations for the manufacture of cement.

3. **Energy industry**

   (a) Industrial installations for the production of electricity, steam and hot water (unless included in Annex I).
   (b) Industrial installations for carrying gas, steam and hot water; transmission of electrical energy by overhead cables.
   (c) Surface storage of natural gas.
   (d) Underground storage of combustible gases.
   (e) Surface storage of fossil fuels.
   (f) Industrial briquetting of coal and lignite.
   (g) Installations for the production or enrichment of nuclear fuels.
   (h) installations for the reprocessing of irradiated nuclear fuels.
   (i) Installations for the collection and processing of radioactive waste (unless included in Annex I).
   (j) Installations for hydroelectric energy production.

4. **Processing of metals**

   (a) Iron and steelworks, including foundries, forges, drawing plants and rolling mills (unless included in Annex I).
   (b) Installations for the production, including smelting, refining, drawing and rolling of non-ferrous metals, excluding precious metals.
   (c) Pressing, drawing and stamping of large castings.
   (d) Surface treatment and coating of metals.
   (e) Boilermaking, manufacture of reservoirs, tanks and other sheet-metal containers.
   (f) Manufacture and assembly of motor vehicles and manufacture of motor-vehicle engines.
   (g) Shipyards.
   (h) Installations for the construction and repair of aircraft.
   (i) Manufacture of railway equipment.
   (j) Swaging by explosives.
   (k) Installations for the roasting and sintering of metallic ores.

5. **Manufacture of glass**

6. **Chemical industry**

   (a) Treatment of intermediate products and production of chemicals (unless included in Annex I).
   (b) Production of pesticides and pharmaceutical products, paint and varnishes, elastomers and peroxides.
   (c) Storage facilities for petroleum, petrochemical and chemical products.

7. **Food industry**

   (a) Manufacture of vegetable and animal oils and fats.
   (b) Packing and canning of animal and vegetable products.
   (c) Manufacture of dairy products.
   (d) Brewing and malting.
   (e) Confectionery and syrup manufacture.
   (f) Installations for the slaughter of animals.
   (g) Industrial starch manufacturing installations.
   (h) Fish-meal and fish oil factories.
   (i) Sugar factories.

8. **Textile, leather, wood and paper industries**

   (a) Wool scouring, degreasing and bleaching factories.
   (b) Manufacture of fibre board, particle board and plywood.
   (c) Manufacture of pulp, paper and board.
   (d) Fibre-dyeing factories.
   (e) Cellulose-processing and production installations.
   (f) Tannery and leather-dressing factories.

9. **Rubber industry**

   Manufacture and treatment of elastomer-based products.

10. **Infrastructure projects**

    (a) Industrial-estate development projects.
    (b) Urban-development projects.
    (c) Ski-lifts and cable-cars.
    (d) Construction of roads, harbours, including fishing harbours, and airfields (projects not listed in Annex I).
    (e) Canalization and flood-relief works.
    (f) Dams and other installations designed to hold water or store it on a long-term basis.
    (g) Tramways, elevated and underground railways, suspended lines or similar lines of a particular type, used exclusively or mainly for passenger transport.
    (h) Oil and gas pipeline installations.
    (i) Installation of long-distance aqueducts.
    (j) Yacht marinas.

No L 175/47   Official Journal of the European Communities   5.7.85

11. **Other projects**

   (a) Holiday villages, hotel complexes.

   (b) Permanent racing and test tracks for cars and motor cycles.

   (c) Installations for the disposal of industrial and domestic waste (unless included in Annex I).

   (d) Waste water treatment plants.

   (e) Sludge-deposition sites.

   (f) Storage of scrap iron.

   (g) Test benches for engines, turbines or reactors.

   (h) Manufacture of artificial mineral fibres.

   (i) Manufacture, packing, loading or placing in cartridges of gunpowder and explosives.

   (j) Knackers' yards.

12. Modifications to development projects included in Annex I and projects in Annex I undertaken exclusively or mainly for the development and testing of new methods or products not used for more than one year.

ANNEX III

PROJECTS SUBJECT TO ARTICLE 4 (2)

1. Description of the project, including in particular:

   -- a description of the physical characteristics of the whole project and the land-use requirements during the construction and operational phases.
   -- a description of the main characteristics of the production processes, for instance, nature and quantity of the materials used.
   -- an estimate, by type and quantity, of expected residues and emissions (water, air and soil pollution, noise, vibration, light, heat, radiation, etc.) resulting from the operation of the proposed project.

2. Where appropriate, an outline of the main alternatives studied by the developer and an indication of the main reasons for his choice, taking into account the environmental effects.

3. A description of the aspects of the environment likely to be significantly affected by the proposed project, including, in particular, population, fauna, flora, soil, water, air, climatic factors, material assets, including the architectural and archaeological heritage, landscape and the inter-relationship between the above factors.

4. A description[1] of the likely significant effects of the proposed project on the environment if resulting from:

   -- the existence of the project,
   -- the use of natural resources,
   -- the emission of pollutants, the creation of nuisances and the elimination of waste,

   and the description by the developer of the forecasting methods used to assess the effects on the environment.

5. A description of the measures envisaged to prevent, reduce and where possible offset any significant adverse effects on the environment.

6. A non-technical summary of the information provided under the above headings.

7. An indication of any difficulties (technical deficiencies or lack of know-how) encountered by the developer in compiling the required information.

---

[1] This description should cover the direct effects and any indirect, secondary, cumulative, short, medium and long-term, permanent and temporary, positive and negative effects of the project.

Annex A. Local association submissions

A1.   EAST ANGLIAN ASSOCIATION

Conversion of old sewage treatment
works to Biodisc
The Dip, Felixstowe: coast protection
works Chelmsford bypass
Clacton sea defence scheme

A2.   EAST MIDLANDS ASSOCIATION

National environment city
Leicester CHP project
Combined heat and power unit,
St Margaret's Baths, Leicester
Nottinghamshire County Council:
environmental improvements in urban
areas
Cold recycling of road materials
Methane from waste tips, Enderby
Warren Quarry

A3.   EDINBURGH AND EAST OF SCOTLAND

Eastern link road, Dunfermline
Glenfarg water treatment plant
Lochore Meadows: land reclamation
project
Megget Reservoir scheme
Powderhall refuse disposal works

A4.   GLASGOW AND WEST OF SCOTLAND

Inverness tyre wall
Aonach Mor ski centre
Use of River Clyde dredgings as topsoil

A5.   HOME COUNTIES ASSOCIATION

A1(M) Hatfield tunnel project
Buntingford high street improvement
scheme
Sevenoaks wild fowl reserve
Reclamation of derelict land
Oxford park and ride
Greenland south docks

A6.   MIDLANDS ASSOCIATION

Canals: walkway improvements
Reclamation of derelict land
Urban renewal, Birmingham
Shropshire groundwater scheme, Severn
Trent Water

A7.   NORTHERN IRELAND ASSOCIATION

The proposed new Lagan Weir, Belfast

A8.   NORTH WESTERN ASSOCIATION

The A55 North Wales coast road
The Old Brickworks, Llandudno Junction

A9.   SOUTHERN ASSOCIATION

BP oil development at Wytch Farm

A10.   SOUTH EASTERN ASSOCIATION

The Channel Tunnel Ashford ring road
Hythe long sea outfall scheme
Water resources development, Botswana

A11.   SOUTH WALES ASSOCIATION

Cardiff Bay
Ebbw Vale Garden Festival site
Duport Steelworks, Llanelli
Llanelli wildfowl centre

A12.   SOUTH WESTERN ASSOCIATION

Maintinaining river quality during
construction of large projects

A1. East Anglian Association

Conversion of old sewage treatment works to Biodisc

A1.1. A programme of conversion has been introduced by Suffolk Coastal District Council to replace the old Housing Act sewage treatment works with Biodisc sewage treatment works. The old plant was above ground and inefficient, produced effluent which caused the local nuisance of smell and involved high maintenance costs to the council.

A1.2. Various options to deal more effectively with the sewage were considered and Biodisc and similar systems were found to have many advantages. The implemented schemes have cost about £35,000 and have replaced the old works with covered semi-below ground energy and biologically efficient and unobtrusive plant. Operation of the plant is completely contained producing a safe effluent, and economically it has low capital and maintenance costs. A measure of environmental acceptability has been the decline in the number of complaints.

A1.3. The programme has been so successful that it is being adopted as a low cost environmentally acceptable solution to first time sewerage schemes for rural villages. Traditional treatment works or pumping to other existing distant STW would not be economic; while the scheme also overcomes the septicity problems of long pipelines, which causes serious odour and corrosion and needs expensive chemical dosing to cure.

The Dip, Felixstowe: coast protection works

A1.4. The coast protection works at the Dip, Felixstowe, became necessary following the collapse of cliffs during a severe storm in 1986. The site is a piece of exposed coastline dominated by clay cliffs. The total construction cost was £2.9M, promoted by Suffolk Coastal District Council. The scheme had to cope with the difficult landscape of natural slippage of cliffs threatening the local amenity beach area.

A1.5. The cliff was regraded to achieve long-term stability to an overall slope of 1 in 3.5, and terraces accommodate beach huts and access routes. To protect the cliff toe, a stepped concrete revetment has been built of precast elements where possible to minimise wave reflections at the lower levels and landtake at the higher levels. To reduce their weight and provide resistance to wave forces they are cast with projecting reinforcement to anchor them to the *in situ* concrete fill beneath. The revetment has greatly improved the amenity of the area and the groyne field was constructed of hardwoods from a managed renewable source.

A1.6. Beach replenishment is now being extended to the adjacent Felixstowe beaches to form a natural protection to the toe of the cliffs, and in the low lying areas to protect the flood wall. The resultant sand/shingle beach also enhances the amenity value of the seafront. Previous facilities were restored, including a boat park, access ramps for the disabled and beach huts. Landscaping involved the planting of species indigenous to the coastline to soften the impact of the heavy protective structure and to harmonise with the environment of the area.

POLLUTION

Chelmsford bypass

A1.7. The Chelmsford bypass represents a major civil engineering achievement involving two decades of planning and design. It has had a beneficial impact on the nation's infrastructure and lives of the local communities, improving traffic conditions in and around Chelmsford and throughout central Essex.

A1.8. The A12 Chelmsford Bypass completes a length of dual carriageway trunk road from London through Essex and Sussex providing access to the ports of East Anglia. The bypass is 14.8km long, built to dual two-lane all-purpose road standard and incorporates five grade-separated interchanges. Traffic has almost halved on the old bypass, route journey times have been drastically cut, rat-runs through residential areas and villages have been eliminated, traffic conditions in Chelmsford have improved and the reliability of emergency services and the buses have increased.

A1.9. Environmental issues played a major part in the choice of route and every effort was made to minimise the adverse effects the bypass would have on the predominantly pastoral landscape. A southern route was preferred to one through the built up area as less environmentally damaging to the locality. The main and side roads were kept as low as possible which entailed increased costs of land purchase and excavation. The surplus soil was used to construct 2km of amenity bunds which have been returned to agriculture and further conceal the road from local communities.

A1.10. Horizontal alignment of the route was adjusted to fit into the landscape whilst avoiding features such as the ornamental lake at Boreham House, a Grade 1 listed building. The Department's planting proposals will further prevent the road from causing visual intrusion.

A1.11. Further unusual activities have been introduced to minimise environmental harm, including

(a) provision of a pipe for badgers to cross the bypass, with appropriate fencing to encourage its use
(b) planting single row hedges in addition to the normal boundary fence
(c) creation of a small pond where a stream flows through Boreham Interchange
(d) trial-seeding of a cutting slope with a special wildflower mix
(e) making provision for the benefit and safety of horseriders
(f) seeking specialised architectural advice on the design of structure, i.e. Chelmer Bridge, intended to be aesthetically pleasing in an attractive river valley.

A1.12. Every opportunity was taken to maintain the quality of the environment, although noise will adversely affect a number of people. However, such disbenefits must be weighed against the permanent environmental benefits to Chelmsford.

Clacton sea defence scheme

A1.13. In 1953, the sea wall was breached on the Essex coast at Jaywick, 35 people were drowned and 600 made homeless. Since that disaster, major breaches have only been narrowly averted and minor flooding occurs annually.

A1.14. The sea wall protecting a 4km length of sea front from Clacton on Sea to Jaywick was inadequate. The oldest section of the wall had been built in the 1930s and the continual buffeting from the North Sea had eroded the protective beach in front of the wall. The sea wall's toe piles had been exposed and worn away by the ever moving shingle.

136

This lowering of the beach level increased the depth of the water in front of the wall which resulted in greater wave heights.

A1.15. The total effect was to undermine the stability of the wall, increase damage due to wave overtopping, and produce tidal currents close inshore which moved the beach material. It was a potentially dangerous situation requiring urgent remedial action.

A1.16. Conventional improvements to the sea walls would have been necessary on a much larger scale than previous schemes and would have been both expensive and environmentally undesirable. Traditional groynes were considered and rejected as unsympathetic to the environment.

A1.17. The adopted scheme works with nature to provide natural environment on the beach. The structure captures suspended material in longshore/littoral drifts to supplement beaches. The sea wall at Jaywick was reconstructed and the natural beach rebuilt with large rock-armoured breakwaters to protect the new beach from future erosion. This is only the second such scheme to be designed in this country and involved extensive on-site measurements, recording, surveys, numerical modelling and advice from specialist consultants. The total cost was £11M and construction took place in 1986-88.

A1.18. The completed scheme protects an area of 200ha from flooding to a 1 in 1,000 year standard. The protected area includes 2,000 houses and several hundred holiday chalets and caravans. In addition, the general amenity value of the area has been greatly enhanced. The total discounted benefits are £15M giving a benefit:cost ratio of 1.4:1. Indirect benefits could double this figure.

A2. East Midlands Association

National environment city

A2.1. Leicester has recently begun work on an environmental protection strategy and based on this and previous initiatives, Leicester will be making a bid to become the National Environment City.

A2.2. Leicester City Council has promoted an ecology strategy, emphasising the benefits of landscaping and the provision of habitats for wildlife in urban areas. Development has led to open land becoming increasingly scarce. The ecology strategy aims to promote nature conservation as a legitimate land use in the city. A city wide strategy is required to

(a)   protect the best wildlife sites and enhance the ecological, recreational, educational and visual quality of open spaces in the city

(b)   provide a network of natural green spaces with improved access to the countryside

(c)   improve the attractiveness of Leicester to visitors and investors

(d)   improve the quality of life for residents of the city.

A2.3. Leicester City Council has been pioneering the efficient use of energy since the early 1970s. In the past ten years it has reduced its energy consumption by some 15% - despite the fact that it now has many more energy consuming buildings and provides more services than in 1979. The council's investment in energy efficiency has reduced carbon dioxide emissions by 90,000 tonnes in the past ten years and has also virtually halved its energy bill. The council has also promoted the use of renewable energy resources by installing solar energy collectors in swimming pools and houses and by investigating the feasibility of wind turbine generators at New Walk Centre.

Leicester CHP project

A2.4. The term CHP (combined heat and power) is used to define the process of utilising plant to generate both electricity and usable heat thereby extracting the maximum benefit from the fuel used. When electricity is generated as the sole product, no more than 40% of the fuel is converted into useful power, the rest of the energy is dissipated as low grade waste heat. However, in the combined production of heat and electricity up to 85% of the fuel energy can be converted into saleable products, about 30% into electricity and up to 55% into heat.

The extent of CHP use in Western Europe

Country	Number of Towns with CHP plants
FRG	57
Finland	35
Denmark	20
Sweden	17
Austria	10
Italy	7
Belgium	4
Switzerland	4
France	4
Netherlands	4
UK	1

A2.5. CHP plants use energy far more efficiently and generate both electricity and heat, reducing carbon dioxide emissions. Leicester Energy Limited was formed jointly by public and private organisations to promote a city wide CHP project. This large co-generation scheme would provide heat to major buildings in the city, and electricity which could be sold to a privatised electricity distribution company. The £80M scheme is currently awaiting the results of the privatisation of the electricity industry.

A2.6. The Leicester CHP project will be run by an independent combined heat and power company. This company will generate electricity and heat and will supply the heat to houses, offices and factories in the Leicester area. It is planned to extend its network so that, in time, the whole of Leicester can be supplied with heat. The power station site is close to the city centre and screening and landscaping will be undertaken. Emissions will comply with the current and anticipated European standards. The routing of hot water pipes will aim to minimise disruption.

A2.7. The customers will include hospitals, the university and polytechnic, city and county council premises, commercial property and four city council housing developments which currently operate group heating schemes.

Combined heat and power unit, St Margaret's Baths Leicester

A2.8. Mini CHP units are now being used more widely and an example is at St Margaret's Baths, Leicester, where electricity is generated for use in the building whilst at the same time heat is provided for the baths. It was installed in November 1989 at a cost of £40,000 with an estimated payback period of 2.5 years. The gas fired unit generates 75kW of electricity and 135kW of heat for use at the baths. This co-generation makes more efficient use of energy than burning gas in a boiler and using electricity from a conventional power station, thereby resulting in dramatic reductions in carbon dioxide emissions. St Margaret's Baths is producing approximately 18 tonnes of carbon dioxide less per year than it did before the CHP unit was installed.

Nottinghamshire County Council: environmental improvements in urban areas

A2.9. Nottinghamshire County Council has carried out many schemes in recent years to improve both urban and rural areas. A special group of professional engineers, landscape architects and technical staff undertake effective environmental improvements. Almost £10M has been spent on these projects, of which the following are examples:

(a) Mansfield Woodhouse, Albert Square, was fronted by run down but potentially attractive stone buildings. The square was formed by the junction of three converging roads, and consisted of 2000m² of tarmac. The large redundant areas were reclaimed and a combination of paving and trees and private investment to the houses has restored the character of this district.

(b) In Victorian days, Queens Road was a graceful entrance to the city from the south. The redevelopment of the meadows removed the need for the road and presented the opportunity to create a pleasant walk from the city centre to the Trent embankment together with a route for cyclists.

(c) Annesley Village consisted of two rows of terraced houses separated by a 4.5ha central area. Housing stock was decaying and the flat central area once used for allotments was being used for parking and tipping and had become rat-infested. The whole area was cleared and the ground contoured to produce a rolling landscaped area. Amenity and forestry planting was introduced, and new roadworks, rear access tracks and parking facilities have revitalised the village and attracted investment to the housing stock.

(d) Pedestrianisation can rejuvenate areas and attract shoppers to safer cleaner environments. It can lead to an increase in trade, and development in new areas such as craft and catering. The opening of a new supermarket off the High Street at Beeston together with a ban on traffic brought opposition from traders fearing a loss of trade, and also the continued illegal use of the street by vehicles. In 1987 the area was repaved and traffic patterns were reorganised to prevent access. The scheme has been nationally commended and has brought a massive increase in the use of the area. A particular attraction is the sculpture 'Beeston Seat and the Beekeeper'.

Cold recycling of road materials

A2.10. To reduce the demand for quarries and tree-felling, the economics of re-using materials such as roadstone is attractive whilst also helping to protect the environment. New performance specifications are being developed by Leicestershire County Council which will encompass the use of recycled materials of varying quality, e.g. road planings could be used for strip widening on minor roads with a thin layer of asphalt to provide the running surface. The cold recycling of road materials *in situ* could be used for reshaping lightly trafficked urban streets.

A2.11. Leicester City Council are using such recycling methods more extensively on footways and carriageways. Previously the reconstruction of bituminous footways involved the excavation of old material and its replacement with new.

A2.12. The *in situ* recycling of footways comprises the grinding down of the original blacktop surfacing materials to a depth of 75mm. Bitumen emulsion is added to bind the materials together and large particles are removed. The material is rolled out and a final 15mm bituminous wearing course is applied. The new process has resulted in a 30% saving in cost and a saving in the use of new materials.

Methane from waste tips, Enderby Warren Quarry

A2.13. The development of this major landfill site in Enderby required the control and treatment of leachate and coping with the safety aspects of methane. The control of methane was achieved by installing a grid of gas wells connected to a gas flarestack. Development of this gas as a resource will be carried out by Leicestershire County Council and Base Load Systems Ltd, who propose to generate electricity on site for sale to the national grid. It is planned to increase the initial generation of 1.5MW of power to 4.5MW. It is hoped that income to the county council from this previously untapped source of methane will exceed £100,000.

A3. Edinburgh and East of Scotland

Eastern link road, Dunfermline

A3.1.   The town centre of Dunfermline suffered from noise, severance and pollution due to poor traffic circulation. The Eastern Link Road was constructed to solve these problems but had to be built in an environmentally sensitive area. It aimed to improve the environment of the town, particularly the shopping and residential areas, and reduce town centre traffic with improved traffic flow and reduced delay at junctions.

A3.2.   Much of the new road is located in a major park and considerable care was taken to minimise the impact of it on park users and local residents. The design has recognised the need to blend into the surrounding environment with detailed attention to concrete finishes to structure and the replacement of features such as car parks and children's play area. A considerable amount of landscaping was carried out to reinstate and improve the adjacent public park after the road was opened to traffic. Pedestrians using and crossing the public park or travelling to and from Dunfermline railway station have been provided with two footbridges and two underpasses, which are aesthetically attractive.

A3.3.   The Link Road provides a major part of the final road system in Dunfermline which will include pedestrianised streets, service only roads and local distributor roads enabling the town to achieve its full business potential.   The standard of workmanship on roads and structures and the detailed attention to landscaping has resulted in an overall enhancement of the area and an improvement in the road network. The scheme is both functional and aesthetically pleasing.

Glenfarg water treatment plant

A3.4.   The problem of rising demand for water in the Fife and Kinross region could not be met by the existing sources which includes Glenfarg Reservoir. This impounding reservoir used slow sand filters and could not be extended to a sufficient extent. The problem was solved by the River Earn Water Supply Scheme, which involved the pumping of 68ml/day from the River Earn to the Glenfarg Reservoir and the construction of a new water treatment plant in this environmentally sensitive area.

A3.5.   The intake works at the River Earn were sited at the tidal reach of the River Tay, where they would be unobtrusive. They were not affected by salinity and allowed for levels of water to remain unaltered to permit migrating salmon and sea trout a passage to their spawning grounds. The new treatment works were sited in a glen of outstanding natural beauty in the Perthshire mountains. A rapid gravity water treatment plant was identified as the best solution and the buildings were designed to be rural in character under the theme of a farmyard concept to blend in with the landscape.

A3.6.   Environmental considerations have governed the whole scheme from the siting of the intake works and utilising an existing impounding reservoir, to the location and design of the treatment works. The whole area has been suitably landscaped and the overall aim has been to provide a reasonably natural intrusion into the landscape.

**Lochore Meadows:
land reclamation project**

A3.7.   The Lochore Meadows Project is one of the most comprehensive land reclamation projects completed in Europe. It has been regarded as the classic Scottish example of environmental rejuvenation. It has improved the quality of life of the local community, suffering from the effects of urban decay and widespread dereliction following closure of the local mines, raised general amenity standards, and provided new opportunities for agriculture, industrial development and countryside recreation.

A3.8. This project was undertaken by the Fife local authorities as the principal component of the environmental improvement programme. Its basic objectives were to remove the dereliction of the coal mining industry and provide a renewed landscape, with productive agricultural land, land for industrial re-use and a regional recreational park.

A3.9. The derelict land extended over 600ha and included six recently worked-out mines. The landscape consisted of decaying colliery buildings and pithead machinery, disused mineral railways and large areas of flooding and subsidence including at its centre a large expanse of water called Loch Ore. There were also enormous spoilheaps, some over 60m high.

A3.10. The work involved demolition and clearance of buildings and structures, capping of pit shafts, drainage of flooded land and realignment of water courses. The regrading of burning bings was necessary; these comprised of an outer crust with inner materials burning at temperatures of up to 1,000°C. Innovative techniques were devised to regrade the burning material with minimal combustion on exposure to the air. This enabled the final stage of regrading and formation of contours, spreading of topsoil, fertilisation and sowing of grass and tree planting.

A3.11. In all 400ha were allocated to country park use and the Mary Colliery pithead winding gear was retained as part of the area's mining heritage. Infrastructure to support the park was constructed and facilities for fishing, sailing, canoeing, wind-surfing, golfing and pony trekking were provided. In 1976 it was registered as a country park by the Countryside Commission for Scotland.

A3.12. A further 190ha were put into agricultural use and were leased to adjacent farms for grazing. This has improved the viability of these farms by providing additional pasture, giving good productivity in livestock rearing. The remaining 10ha of the reclaimed land was designed as an industrial estate. It was taken over by Dunfermline District Council who provided site services and access roads. About half the site is currently developed and has attracted small businesses contributing to the generation of local employment.

A3.13. The Lochore Meadows Land Reclamation Project has brought new life and purpose to economically, socially and environmentally deprived communities and has been vital in increasing their future viability and prosperity. It has transformed an area of colliery waste into pleasantly contoured agricultural land.

Megget Reservoir scheme

A3.14. The Megget Reservoir Scheme has received substantial national recognition, winning the 1986 Financial Times Architecture at Work Award and the 1987 Environmental Section of the BBC Design Awards.

A3.15. The reservoir is located near Selkirk and represents a fully integrated piece of infrastructure in balance with its remote upland environment. The fusion of environment and design is the result of the successful partnership between the consulting engineers and landscape architects.

A3.16. The Megget Scheme is a major development of the River Tweed, designed to meet the estimated water requirements of the Lothian Region in two stages for a period of about 50 years ahead. As part of the design process, a thorough programme of environmental assessment of the potential impact of the reservoir was carried out. This approach established the means to alleviate detrimental effects and dentify new opportunities for landscape design, nature conservation and recreation.

A3.17. Care has been taken in the design of the scheme, to respect the qualities of the upland landscape and to enhance it where possible. The reservoir, in conjunction with the outlet control works at St Mary's Loch, also provides considerable control on the downstream river discharges to the benefit of fishery and other interests, and also eases flooding.

Powderhall refuse disposal works

A3.18. For over a century, refuse disposal in Edinburgh was carried out at the Powderhall incineration works. However, the implications of moving the city's refuse by road transfer to landfill sites have grown increasingly serious. The new scheme involved the replacement of the incineration works with a large transfer station.

A3.19. Maximum use was made in the new design of storage bunkers, cranes and buildings associated with the earlier plant. Rail sidings and other works constructed at Powderhall and at Kaimes Quarry landfill site allowed for 450 tonnes of refuse to be moved each day in one train from Powderhall. Five trains per week will run consisting of 11 container wagons each carrying 1 x 6m long containers and each carrying approximately 13.5 tonnes of domestic waste every trip.

A3.20. This is the first contract of its kind in Scotland for the transportation of domestic refuse from the centre of the city to landfill by rail. It will remove the need for a fleet of heavy container lorries travelling through congested city centre streets and will allow for future development of major landfill sites some distance from the city centre.

A4. Glasgow and West of Scotland

Inverness tyre wall

A4.1.   The disposal of waste tyres is a major problem due to improved manufacturing techniques and legislation which prevents burning. Since 1905 the refuse of Inverness has been tipped on the foreshore slowly reclaiming land for future development. Coastal protection has generally been achieved by tipping heavy inert material along the seaward edge. Following earlier experiments in England and America it was decided to collect disused tyres in Inverness and use them for the construction of a retaining wall to provide coastal protection at the town's refuse tip at Longman.

A4.2.   Sir William Halcrow and Partners adapted earlier designs. The split tyres were tied together with polypropylene rope and each layer filled with sand and gravel taken from the foreshore. Each layer was compacted with a vibrating roller and as successive layers were placed, the near vertical 2.85m wall was built. Lorry tyres formed the core and were tied to about 21,000 car tyres at the face to build the 340mm long wall.

A4.3.   The wall took approximately four months to build in 1985; its appearance is environmentally acceptable and it has stood up to substantial wave action. It has made excellent use of a waste material and was an extremely cost effective solution at £68,000.

Aonach Mor ski centre

A4.4.   This ski centre is situated on the north slopes of Ben Nevis near Fort William. As it crosses two sites of special scientific interest (SSSIs), meticulous attention to the environmental impact of the project was required. The Institute of Terrestrial Ecology surveyed the area and assessed the impact of development, and with regulation on construction reinstatement and minimum disturbance, damage to the delicate mountain environment was avoided.

A4.5.   Materials had to be transported by helicopter due to a ban on vehicles driving up the mountain. Great care was taken at each of the pylon foundations to remove the natural heather turf and keep it for replacing. The mini excavators digging the foundations used mats to avoid tracking the hillside and surplus excavations were removed before the turf was replaced.

A4.6.   British Alcan, who own the land, were concerned that serious damage could be caused to their power station turbines at the foot of the mountain by sediments, released in the run-off water from erosion caused by skiers and piste bashing machines. The collector tunnel for the hydro scheme passes directly below the ski area and takes about 0.5% of its water run-off from the catchment. The run-off is collected behind interceptor dams built on the hillside before delivery down shafts to the main tunnel. Settlement tanks in front of these dams ensure acceptable water standards are met. These preventative measures alone added £200,000 to the project cost.

A4.7.   The £2.6M contract was completed in ten months and the alpine construction techniques have satisfied the demanding environmental standards protecting the delicate mountain environment of Britain's highest mountain.

Use of River Clyde dredgings as topsoil

A4.8. The study undertaken by Strathclyde University Civil Engineering Department into the feasibility of producing topsoil from dredgings from the River Clyde has proved that topsoil can be manufactured commercially from dredged spoil. Sufficient material exists to satisfy a significant proportion of local topsoil demands in the foreseeable future. It has also demonstrated that disposal at sea of dredged spoil is not always necessary, and thereby provided a solution to a problem which may arise with the new European legislation regulating dumping at sea of waste materials. The three year study has identified the problems and solutions associated with the reuse of dredged spoil and won a commendation in the Better Environment Awards for Industry in 1987.

A4.9. The major problems included the quantity, quality, marketing and physical characteristics of the sediments; the growth characteristics; the dredging and handling of the sediments; the drying-mixing problems; the identification of an acceptable topsoil specification; and the cost of the reprocessing in relation to the value of the Clydesoil product. With practical quality control, the dredged sediment quality can be processed into a topsoil satisfactory for the full range of soil use as specified by the DoE trigger concentrations. Heavy metal concentrations and the presence of organic compounds in the crude sediments are only significant in the clay and silt fractions and can be overcome when mixed with coarse sediments, or with other materials such as pulverised fuel ash. The level of cadmium, zinc, acidity and salinity in the topsoil product is sensitive but readily controllable in the soil manufacturing process.

A4.10. The River Clyde system contains an estimated 1.675Mm^3 dredgable *in situ* material of which 57% is fine grained silts and clays and 43% is granular fine to coarse sands. The upper Clyde is replenished with sediments at an average rate of 100,000 tonnes dry weight per year.

A4.11. A practical method using existing dredging plant was developed to handle up to 100,000 tonnes dry weight per year for land disposal. Further cost savings could be obtained by replacing the present system with modern customer built plant. The dredged sediments can be dried using natural evaporation and a sand filter bed. A six month lead time and adequate storage space is necessary to allow for marketing of the product.

A4.12. The growth potential of the Clydesoil supports the full range of grasses, trees and plants used in the structured planting of the Glasgow Garden Festival. It also supports a range of exotic plants and flowers and is initially weed free.

A4.13. The study was conducted within the original SDA budget of £189,023. It has produced savings in the cost of dredging for Clydeport, with a potential revenue of £200,000/year. It also saved up to 10% on dredging costs, provided a total of almost 30,000 tonnes dry weight of soil worth £120,000 for a number of sites; and promoted dredging of the dock basin of Babcock Power.

A5.   Home Counties Association

A1(M) Hatfield tunnel project

A5.1.   Environmental issues were a prime consideration in the choice of route for the final stage of the improvement to the A1 to motorway standard as it passes through Hertfordshire. This last remaining section through Hatfield proved to be the most difficult because of its largely urban nature and the conflicting demands of highway, environment and local needs.

A5.2.   The existing route had become overloaded and suffered from frequent and long delays. The daily routes of local residents were constantly congested and the general environment polluted with noise and fumes. The area was generally becoming run down and unlikely to attract the necessary urban renewal. Against this background, efforts were made to resolve the conflict between traffic and environment in a postive and creative manner.

A5.3.   Off-line surface routes duplicating the existing route were dismissed due to their harmful effect on the environment and landtake problems. The best highway solution lay along the existing route but the environmental effects were potentially disastrous requiring the demolition of existing property and exposing the remaining property to environmental pollution.

A5.4.   Measures were devised to shield the new route from the town. The section passing closest to the built up area was constructed immediately alongside the existing route in a 1,150m long cut and fill tunnel. The existing road staying to form the local road.

A5.5.   This protected the developed area of Hatfield from the effects of the new motorway, which created the opportunity to re-develop a 10ha site. The new motorway was opened to traffic on 10 December 1986 and work on the vast redevelopment scheme should be completed in spring 1991.

Buntingford High Street improvement scheme

A5.6.   The opening of a bypass removed A10 traffic from the centre of Buntingford in Hertfordshire and provided an opportunity to improve the town's High Street.

A5.7.   The aim has been to enhance the local environment mainly by implementing a scheme more favourable to pedestrians than vehicles without introducing total pedestrianisation. The speed of any traffic which needs to use the High Street has been greatly reduced by the use of throttle points and speed tables. Delivery to shops by heavy goods vehicles has been limited by weight restrictions and by one way access arrangements. Special limited waiting parking bays have been created. Throughout attention has been paid to the type of construction materials used. These have been selected to keep with the period architecture of the town. The creation of community areas has also been a particular feature.

Sevenoaks wild fowl reserve

A5.8.   The extraction of sand and gravel aggregates is necessary for use on construction sites and the manufacture of ready mixed concrete. Land restoration is now an essential corollary of sand and gravel extraction. Expertise in planning and coordinating the agricultural restoration of sites is required to create areas of landscaped water and nature conservation.

A5.9. The internationally renowned Sevenoaks wild fowl reserve in Kent was created by Redland Aggregates in association with the Wild Fowl Trust. The conservation area was created from gravel and sand workings, and has been enlarged to include a wetland and marshland area. 13,000 trees were planted on the reserve including alder, willow and birch, chosen because of their value as a food source for wild fowl and their suitability for the site soil conditions. Plants were also encouraged to grow around the edge of the lakes to give shelter and food for wild fowl.

Reclamation of derelict land

A5.10. Grandpont Gasworks Site consisted of a 10ha site of cleared and severely polluted land near to the city centre and River Thames. Reclamation comprised of sealing the whole area with clay spoil from the Oxford trunk sewer. The land was then developed as a park with extensive landscaping and the old railway bridge converted into a pedestrian bridge. A housing scheme for single persons has been completed with a communal garden.

A5.11. Burgess Field Nature Park was created on the site of a 30ha waste disposal tip. The tip was filled and a community project is transforming the site into a nature park with 20,000 trees, grazing paddocks, butterfly garden and picnic areas.

A5.12. Mouchel were appointed by Esso to design the service station on the M25 near to the Dartford Tunnel. The 40ha site consists of an old quarry infilled with industrial refuse, including asbestos and heavy metals, actively producing landfill gas, mostly methane. The development on this dangerous site will consist of an amenity building, motel, fuel forecourt and parking area.

A5.13. Below the amenity building, pre-cast concrete piles have been driven through the wastefill into the chalk. The area for the petrol forecourt has been excavated down to the chalk to remove the possibility of settlement below the petrol storage tanks and the pit lined with clay and filled with Thanet sand. The ground for the parking area has been stabilised by dynamic compaction. Flint modules have been spread over the surface to help distribute the load and even out future settlement and an inert capping material has been used to level out the surface.

A5.14. The gas control system has been designed to ensure that all risk of explosion, flammability, toxicity and odour is eliminated. The areas supporting a building will have more stringent control than the remainder of the site. All buildings will have a vented void space beneath the floors and special service entries to prevent gas entering, in addition to an active gas extraction system in the surrounding fill. The gas collection system for the car park will be on a horizontal plane close to the surface of the waste and the collector pipes will be flexible polyethylene to accommodate large vertical strains. A fail safe system has been designed which will activate all alarms in the case of emergency.

A5.15. The prime objective of the design team has been to introduce the appropriate technique to each specific area of the site to ensure absolute safety and ultimately create a comfortable stop-over on the M25 motorway.

Oxford park and ride

A5.16. Oxford's Balanced Transport Policy aims to create an efficient transport system and preserve the internationally renowned university and college buildings and their surroundings and other areas of the city within conservation areas, while continuing to enable Oxford to function as a regional and international tourist centre.

A5.17. The construction of new roads would have been severely damaging to the city's unique environment, so the increasing demand for transport into and out of the city has been met through the development of the park and ride service. This comprises four car parks close to the ring road on the edge of the city (where parking is free of charge) and the provision of frequent express bus services serving the city centre. During the 17 years of implementation the number of car parking spaces has grown from 2,000 to 2,500 and during the next year will expand to 3,000. The car parks have been extensively landscaped with trees, shrubs and bulbs and mounded grass areas to ensure that they relate to their rural surroundings.

Greenland south docks

A5.18. The London Docklands Development Corporation aims to retain as much of the history of the area as possible and incorporate it into new works. Gibb were appointed in 1982 to undertake an initial engineering study of the site to design infrastructure enabling the water to be retained in the disued docks. This involved studies of the condition and integrity of dock walls, locks, river walls and bridges. The lock gate and swing bridge machinery were refurbished together with Grade II listed structures and buildings. The river walls were rebuilt and a new dam and lock constructed.

A5.19. A study is now being carried out to recommend the best way of presenting the history of the area to the public - possibly by means of models, diagrams, photographs, display boards and a waterside walk. Developers are now taking possession of the plots of land created by the infrastructure and are building residential, retail and leisure units.

A5.20. Traffic management measures have been incorporated into the new infrastructure to ensure low traffic speeds and greater safety for pedestrians. These measures include special routes for pedestrians and cyclists away from vehicular traffic. Off-street parking facilities have also been included in the design. Traffic regulations associated with these traffic management measures have been introduced.

A6.   Midlands Association

Canals: walkway improvements

A6.1.   Birmingham is at the centre of the country's waterways. The city's canals were once its industrial arteries but fell into disrepair and many lengths became derelict. The city council, in partnership with British Waterways are refurbishing large lengths of canal as a recreational amenity for the people of Birmingham. The Urban Development Division is carrying out a substantial programme of work to towpaths, boundary walls and canal accesses in support of this initiative. The Birmingham Inner City Partnership Walkway Project has opened up areas along the canals for the public. At Canning Walk, the foundations of a demolished chemicals factory were turned into an interesting canal side promenade. Digbeth Branch Canal was declared a conservation area in 1987 and restored by the BICP into an interesting walkway.

Reclamation of derelict land

A6.2.   Due to the economic recession of the 1970s, vast tracts of land have been laid waste by the demise of large industries. In 1982, 866ha of land in Birmingham was identified as being waste or derelict. The Urban Development Division in conjunction with the Economic Development Unit have been responsible for undertaking various reclamation schemes which has resulted in attracting new forms of the industry to the city, e.g. Small Heath Business Park and reclamation of Ansells Brewery Site.

Urban renewal, Birmingham

A6.3.   The City of Birmingham has over 100,000 properties built before 1919 with many in serious disrepair and lacking in basic amenities. In 1974 the city council introduced the urban renewal programme to retain and rehabilitate the housing stock and regenerate the area. The City Architect is responsible for property improvement and off-street environmental works. These works consist of all the property repair, maintenance and improvement carried out under city contracts; the construction of new front and rear boundary walls or fences and the reconstruction or repaving of access paths and rear driveways.

A6.4.   The City Engineer implements the on-street environmental works. This is done in close liaison with the Director of Environmental Services and the City Architect to ensure a consistent and coordinated approach. Engineering standards and the aesthetic impact of the works are therefore given proper consideration. The designs have been produced to ensure that vehicles in residential areas travel at slower speeds.

A6.5.   The traditional road surface of black asphalt has been replaced by different and new materials in conjunction with a revised approach to traffic management. The problems of rat-running and parking in residential side roads have been addressed. The general approach has been to change the street scene so that motorists are clearly aware that they are in a residential area. Particular attention has been paid to the entrance to a residential road and the aesthetics within the area. The measures adopted have included carriageway width restrictors, block paving rumble strips, construction of parking bays, traffic management, and street furniture (trees, seats, etc). In the great majority of cases, the measures have been successful and have received a favourable response from residents.

Shropshire groundwater scheme, Severn Trent Water

A6.6. The Shropshire groundwater scheme was designed to meet the increasing water needs of the West Midlands. The River Severn provides the main water supplies, augmented by releases from reservoirs in times of low flow. This scheme enables further water to be pumped from the sandstone beds in North Shropshire into the River Severn during drought conditions. The extraction from the sandstone is replaced by natural rainfall.

A6.7. A multi-disciplinary team investigated environmental considerations such as the lowering of the water table and its effect on vegetation, trees etc, and the effect on the temperature and quality of the water in the river. Detailed consultations were carried out with landowners, farmers and other affected organisations and agreements reached to ensure the most acceptable operating regime.

A6.8. The Shropshire groundwater scheme has enabled the problem of increased demand for water to be solved without any significant environmental impact, which the construction of dams and reservoirs would have entailed. It has also provided the least cost solution. It is almost totally unobtrusive and is complementary to above ground water storage.

A7.   Northern Ireland Association

The proposed new Lagan Weir Belfast

A7.1.   Laganside Corporation plans to regenerate the River Lagan corridor through downtown Belfast with the creation of an attractive waterfront. The construction of the new Lagan Weir at a cost of £10M will provide an impounded reach of water of 5km.

A7.2.   The weir will consist of a solid structure to low tide level with five gated openings between piers. These gates are bottom hinged so they can be lowered or raised to control the water levels.

A7.3.   Low level sluices are to be incorporated in the weir to withdraw lower saline layers from upstream waters to promote circulation and to avoid stagnation. This will avoid the eutrophication of organic material in the muds which causes stagnation and offensive odours.

A7.4.   The weir will incorporate facilities to permit aeration of the incoming tidal water, enhancing its oxygen content and promoting mixing with the lower saline layers. This will ensure adequate oxygen levels for desired water quality during times of low river flow. Fish life and river fauna will benefit. Migratory fish will be encouraged to pass upstream using the fish passes in two of the piers.

A7.5.   Following construction of the weir, dredging will be undertaken to remove much of the highly organic mud deposits in the impoundment and to provide a sufficient depth to facilitate recreational boating. At mean tide level, there will be some 1.3m of water over any gate set in its fully lowered position, increasing to 2.4m at high tide.

A7.6.   An attractive water environment will be created which will encourage riverside development and promote recreational pursuits.

A8.   North Western Association

The A55 North Wales coast road

A8.1.   The A55 North Wales coast road between Llanddulas in Clwyd and Aber in Gwynedd incorporates a variety of measures to lessen environmental impact during and after construction.

A8.2.   The 28km length is divided into seven separate construction contracts and five have been completed. The 6km Conwy Crossing Contract currently under construction is the largest ever to have been let in the UK, and includes Britain's first immersed tube road tunnel. The tunnel under construction through Pen-y-Clip headland, west of Penmaenmawr, will be Britain's longest road tunnel through rock.

A8.3.   Throughout its length, the route avoids high embankments and deep cuttings as far as possible, and to a large extent parallels the existing line of severance created by Robert Stephenson's Chester-Holyhead railway. Realignment of a 3km length of track from just west of Colwyn Bay station has enabled road and railway to pass through the town in a single low-level corridor.

A8.4.   At Conwy, a tunnel was adopted following a lengthy public inquiry at which the impact on the historic castle and walled town of the originally proposed bridge was debated. In the 1820s, the route westward from Telford's bridge, the first to cross the river at this point, had passed through the town walls, as does the existing trunk road pending completion of the tunnel.

A8.5.   Extensive use was made of the railway for delivery of bulk materials during construction, including 300,000 tonnes of PFA, 22,000 tonnes of reinforcement, 60,000 tonnes of cement, 20,000 tonnes of sand and 5,000 tonnes of steel H-piles. Routes available for construction traffic have been closely controlled and the contracts included restrictions on the numbers of lorries permitted to use the existing trunk road through Conwy.

A8.6.   Great care has been taken to screen the new road in urban and rural areas, the latter including part of Snowdonia National Park. Earth moundings have been used where appropriate and extensive soft and hard landscaping has been designed to complement the new construction.

A8.7.   Diversion of the trunk road has relieved the resorts of Colwyn Bay, Conwy, Penmaenmawr and Llanfairfechan of traffic congestion and pollution, and significant development opportunities have resulted. Colwyn Bay's main shopping street has been pedestrianised and similar plans are being discussed for Conwy. At Penmaenmawr, a new seaside promenade has been constructed, and RSPB hope to create a bird reserve on land in the Conwy estuary reclaimed by the disposal of dredged material.

A8.8.   When completed the A55 North Wales Coast Road will stand as a notable achievement. The designers have made skilful use of the old route, and the policy has been economic in land purchase and considerate to the environment.

The Old Brickworks, Llandudno Junction

A8.9.   Gwynedd County Council wanted to provide a discrete area where various 'bad neighbour' trades such as scrapmetal could be accommodated, since there is a severe shortage of suitable sites within the county. The site of the Old Brickworks, Llandudno Junction, had originally been a brickworks and associated clay pit, and was derelict and flooded to an average depth of some 5m. A scrap car dealer occupied the southern unflooded point of the roughly triangular site, and tipping of non-hazardous industrial waste had taken place within the flooded area.

A8.10. During construction of the site, surplus material was tipped into the pit after planning application had been agreed. This left the site with a gently sloping flat surface of approximately 3ha. A screening bund was provided around the north and west sides of the perimeter which was then grass seeded.

A8.11. Gwynedd County Council compulsorily purchased the site and undertook the development of the existing access road with associated drainage, kerbing and lighting, and provision of plot hardstandings and perimeter fencing. The plots were to be unserviced initially, but water, BT and electricity services were provided in the access road, tenants making arrangements for individual connections to the plots to suit their requirements. For the extension of the access road a dry bound macadam construction was specified as it was anticipated that some considerable residual settlements would take place on the filled tip area. In the longer term it is envisaged that the access road will be surfaced with bituminous flexible materials, when the rate of settlement has reduced.

A8.12. The plot hardstandings comprise a 150mm layer of granular sub-base laid on Terram 2000 geotextile fabric. The geotextile was provided to prevent punching through of the underlying fill material which was of a variable nature. A 300mm layer of sub base had initially been proposed for the hardstanding but this had to be reduced to keep the project within acceptable budget limits. The 150 thickness has generally performed satisfactorily although some localised remedial works have been necessary in one of the plots. Perimeter fencing is 1.8m high chain link with security attachments.

A8.13. The site has provided much needed accommodation for a scrap dealer, two road haulage contractors and a coach firm. Landscape planting of the perimeter bund and surrounding area will be undertaken which will provide additional screening from the adjacent A55 trunk road. The scheme has been particularly successful in removing a local eyesore with the additional benefit of creating useful tidy industrial land for business which would otherwise have been difficult to accommodate satisfactorily within the locality.

A9. Southern Association

BP oil development at Wytch Farm

A9.1.   In 1974 a large oilfield was located beneath the Isle of Purbeck, near Wareham and Poole in Dorset. Five years later development by BP Exploration of an even larger field commenced. The size of the Wytch Farm oilfield is comparable with a large oilfield in the North Sea.

A9.2.   The oilfield is located below an area of outstanding natural beauty in one of the most environmentally sensitive areas of Southern England. Adjacent to the Wytch Farm development are two sites of special scientific interest at Rempstone Heath and Poole Harbour. These heathland areas are the habitat of rare reptiles and birds (such as the sand lizard, the smooth snake and the Dartford warbler) and rare plants on Dorset heath.

A9.3.   The environmental constraints have shaped the construction programme so much that every detail has been assessed to minimise disturbance to the environment. Development permission was only granted subject to 300 conditions designed to protect the environment and local interests. To ensure that environmental safeguards would be observed, BP required all contractors on the project to produce method statements before commencing work showing how all the conditions will be satisfied, and all workers were obliged to go on a compulsory induction course before receiving site passes. Environmental staff work with contractors to ensure they kept to their method statements and that construction processes in the field complied with the sensitive environment of the site. The inspectors had the power to stop the work if construction conditions were breached.

A9.4.   To comply with environmental requirements, the size of construction sites was restricted to the absolute minimum. Room at the gathering station site, for example, is insufficient for the storage of materials or car parking, so the workforce was brought in by bus from various locations in Dorset. Height restrictions at the gathering station have meant that distillation columns have had to be divided in two. When pipelines were being laid across sensitive habitats, vegetation was removed as turf and stored for replacement later. Work on the Cleaval pumping station, where water will be pumped from the sea to replace the oil in the reservoirs, had to be completed by mid November to avoid disturbing wintering birds.

A9.5.   Local roads in the area of the gathering station could not cope with construction traffic and one of the conditions of planning permission was that an access road to the gathering station site be built before any major construction work was started. Working space during road building was not allowed to extend beyond the final position of its boundary fence, and plant was only allowed access to the site from each end and one intermediate point.

A9.6.   Rainwater runoff from the well sites could not be drained on to the surrounding countryside and during drilling due to the risk of contamination from oil spills. Construction sites were not allowed to drain on to the surrounding areas as mud could cause serious damage to local wildlife habitats, so if an excavation fills with water it had to be pumped into a tanker. On Furzey Island, where pumping away rainwater could affect the fresh water/salt water balance of the water table with harmful effects on trees and plants, provision has been made to allow BP to pump clean water in, to recharge the underlying water table.

A9.7.   To avoid disturbing one of the few undiseased oyster beds in Britain, a 1.2km long 660mm diameter pipeline from the well sites on Furzey Island to the mainland was laid by directional drilling instead of the alternative of open cut dredging.

A9.8.   The chief accomplishment of the Wytch Farm project has been to demonstrate that a major development is capable of adapting successfully to take account of environmental issues.

A10. South Eastern Association

The Channel Tunnel
Source: Transmanche-Link, Eurotunnel

A10.1. The Channel Tunnel is the largest single construction project to be undertaken in Western Europe this century. The environmental impact is potentially huge, and this fact has been appreciated from the outset.

A10.2. The Channel Tunnel Group (now Eurotunnel) commissioned a thorough Environmental Impact Assessment by independent specialists as part of a submission to Government in 1985. Subsequent detailed studies were initiated by Eurotunnel prior to the start of construction, as a 'base-line' for comparison with the results of an impact monitoring programme carried out by TML. This programme will continue to the project's completion.

A10.3. Planning of the operation had been carefully arranged to minimise disruption to adjacent countryside and habitation. Specific clauses within the Channel Tunnel Act are more stringent than the requirements of the Town and Country Planning Act for particular areas of environmental interest.

A10.4. These aspects were illustrated in the disposal of chalk spoil from a housing development in Minnis Lane, Dover. The developer was causing some damage to footpaths, annoyance to residents adjacent to the site and was travelling through sensitive villages north of Dover, despite planning consent under the Town and Country Planning Act. When TML agreed to accept chalk from this site, the transporting of material was subject to the Channel Tunnel Act. The developer was restricted to one specific route and had to sheet each load and wash lorry wheels before leaving site. In spite of these improvements, TML involvement meant disturbance and damage was blamed on the Channel Tunnel.

A10.5. Possible effects to the marine environment were debated at length by the Government and the most acceptable solution to the disposal of tunnel spoil was the construction of a series of enclosed lagoons for the material. The costly extensive retaining works allowed construction of this artificial platform at the foot of Shakespeare Cliff in a controlled manner. Continuous monitoring of currents, littoral drift and sea bed colonies etc. determines any effects of building of the sea wall.

A10.6. The rural nature of the terminal site had to be destroyed, though part of the ancient attractive woodland known as Biggins Wood was salvaged by moving selected topsoil with its unique mixture of seed varieties and vegetation to another site and planting new native trees.

A10.7. Drainage of the terminal site and its associated slip roads, sidings, etc. was originally intended to be directed into a purpose built lake south of the M20 motorway. Since this would drown large areas of the Seabrook Valley, a site of special scientific interest, the original proposals were amended. The alternative scheme involves tunnelling a large diameter surface water sewer from the Terminal site beneath the town of Folkestone and out to sea.

A10.8. Earthmoving on any scheme creates changes to the environment, such as dust, mud and noise, as well as disturbance caused by transporting material along busy roads and the depletion of local resources. These aspects of environmental damage were significantly reduced in two ways:

(a)   Imported fill material was taken from the disused Snowden Colliery and transported for most of its journey by rail, keeping lorries away from quiet Kent country roads. Removal of a large quantity of tipped minestone has helped to reduce the problem of visual intrusion, poor vegetation and dust.

(b)   Material dredged from the Goodwin sands off the east Kent coast was pumped into the Terminal site along a 6km purpose built pipeline. This operation delivered nearly five million tonnes of sand into the site over a year and saved half a million lorry journeys and sand in Kent's quarries for future users.

A10.9. Damage has been unavoidable in a scheme of this size. Unforeseen and unexpectedly severe storms in the summer of 1988 caused 'flash flooding' which washed away defences and drowned pumps, causing pollution of a trout lake downstream of river diversion works. Negotiations are being held with the farmer concerned.

A10.10. Following a change of wind direction in the spring of 1988, dust caused by earthmoving and ground stabilisation blew over a large number of houses in Cheriton. This continued to be a problem, though intensive use of water bowsers and crop spray jets has helped to reduce dust to manageable proportions. With serious water shortages in 1989 (and possibly 1990) TML negotiated with Folkestone and District Water Company to abstract non-potable water supplies for dust suppression and sand compaction purposes.

A10.11. Pollution of water courses leading into the stream flowing through Folkestone has been caused by silting up by sand and contamination by salt water. Constant negotiations with the Southern Water and National Rivers Authority has helped TML to keep this problem under control. From time to time pollution caused by local industrial plants has been wrongly attributed to this project.

Ashford ring road

A10.12. Ashford's population has roughly doubled since the war to about 50,000. Its compact town centre, based on a staggered crossroads in a narrow medieval High Street, is unsuited to modern volumes of traffic.

A10.13. To ease traffic flow and to permit pedestrianisation of the centre, a one-way ring road was conceived in the 1960s and constructed in the 1970s, together with a series of traffic management schemes in the central area. The ring road has an unusually small circumference of 2,000m. Whilst it undoubtedly eased traffic flow, the ring road is unpopular with many local people, who perceived it as contributing to the degradation of the urban environment in the following ways:

(a)   The encircling of the town centre with a three and four-lane highway has isolated it from the rest of the town and has ruptured the gentle transition from commercial centre to surrounding residential areas, and affected the town's character.

(b)   The nature of the ring road, in particular the shortness of its weaving lengths, encourages aggressive driving, which is a danger and a deterrent to pedestrians and cyclists.

(c)   Difficult access from ring road to town centre greatly increases journey lengths and deters occasional visitors, although there are significant benefits to the shopping environment have been achieved through pedestrianisation.

(d)   Construction of the ring road required the demolition of much high-density older housing close to the centre and the displacement of well established street communities.

(e)   The above factors have encouraged the commercial redevelopment of the central area and the displacement of further modest homes and traditional local enterprises by large multiple retailers and unpopular office developments. Whilst other forces are clearly at work in this process, the ring road as the most tangible feature attracts most of the blame.

A10.14. Moreover, the capacity of the ring road itself is being overtaken by continuing growth. Traffic volumes have broadly tripled since its conception. Its shortness limits its capacity to absorb congestion. It interconnects the town's five principal radial routes and few alternative routes exist at present, though they are projected. At peak times a restriction such as roadworks or an accident on any one of the radial routes, or on the ring road itself, can lead to total gridlock. Thus a scheme which is perceived as having a heavy toll in disbenefits to the urban environment is increasingly seen as failing in its primary objective. However, in response to increasing traffic flows, the County Council has plans to introduce an Urban Traffic Control scheme, which would involve signalisation of the major junctions under computer control, and this should improve both safety and capacity on the ring road.

The Hythe long sea outfall scheme

A10.15. Sewage from the Hythe area was formerly discharged to the English Channel through two short outfalls, at Hythe and West Hythe. By discharging around low water, they resulted in a significant pollution nuisance to the beaches and inshore waters.

A10.16. Between 1984 and 1989, Southern Water implemented a new marine treatment scheme to replace these facilities. It comprises an onshore headworks where preliminary treatment and pumping take place; an outfall discharging 2,500m beyond low water; and a storm overflow discharging 300m beyond low water. Degradation of the sewage takes place by natural processes within the marine environment.

A10.17. Despite the promised amelioration of beach and inshore pollution, the scheme aroused strong local opposition from individuals and groups, including fishermen. Opposition was directed mainly at the principle of marine treatment (in particular the fishermen feared damage to whelk beds). Objectors voiced preference for an onshore scheme incorporating full treatment, and possibly sited on an extensive military firing range on the outskirts of the town. There were also objections to the siting of the headworks. The objections were handled through normal planning procedures, without recourse to a public inquiry. Southern Water's marine treatment scheme prevailed but the headworks were resited as a concession to objectors.

A10.18. Southern Water are undertaking a major before-and-after marine environmental study to evaluate the effects of the scheme. Sampling of seabed sediments and invertebrate fauna is taking place at 21 sites three times yearly before and after commissioning. Opponents of the scheme have conceded improvement to the beach and inshore waters but continue to object to effects on the marine environment, notably heavy metal and other inorganic pollution of the seabed and contamination of offshore waters.

A10.19. Examination of a number of minor schemes has shown that many involve both positive and negative environmental impact, the former usually predominating. However, the relatively minor environmental disbenefits are often seized upon as a focus for opposition on environmental grounds. Good public consultation often engenders a more balanced attitude to proposals.

Water resources development, Botswana

A10.20. The recently issued EC directives on Environmental Impact Assessment advocate the examination of environmental impacts at the earliest possible stage of project development and this is becoming normal practice in Europe and elsewhere. However, in the developing world the pressures for rapid development of natural resources and infrastructure are such that the assessment of environmental impacts is often afforded low priority. In Botswana, Environmental Impact Assessment has recently been introduced as an essential element in all significant water resource development studies.

A10.21. The Water Utilities Corporation of Botswana engaged consulting engineers to prepare a scheme to augment the existing water supplies to the capital Gaborone. The consulting engineers proposed the construction of two dams in rural areas 30-40km from the city. In 1986, when the contract for the construction of these two dams was out to tender, the Ministry of Local Government and Lands engaged WLPU Consultants to undertake an environmental impact study of the proposed scheme.

A10.22. The study identified adverse impacts downstream of the dams associated with the reduction in water and water suspended nutrients on 180km of river, of which the first 60km would be most affected. It was envisaged that the reduction of water in the river would reduce the recharge to existing village borehole water supplies and thus require sinking of additional boreholes in order to sustain yields. In addition, along the initial 60km of river, flood flows support some 3,000ha of important riverine grazing and wetlands, and an important chain of events was perceived to hinge on maintenance of the natural flood regime. The environmental impact of the loss of wetland grazing would result in a reduction in the availability of animal draught power and cause delay in arable cultivation at the beginning of the rainy season. Many households would be likely to experience economic loss and would be encouraged to seek urban employment; directly contrary to the Botswana Government's aims.

A10.23. The WLPU study, however, assessed an alternative dam site at the downstream end of the critical 60km reach of river which would result in significantly less severe environmental impacts on the groundwater resources and the wetland ecology. In addition, this alternative dam site proved to be a technically and economically more favourable solution and has now been implemented instead of the original proposals.

A11. South Wales Association

Cardiff Bay

A11.1. Cardiff Bay is a wide estuary of about a mile across. At low tide the bay consists of unattractive mud flats which provide a feeding ground for some wading birds. The derelict land extends to the north east of the bay. Much of the coastal area around the bay suffers from industrial dereliction, due largely to the decline of Cardiff as a coal port. The site includes the docklands, a former gasworks and an extensive landfill site used for the disposal of refuse.

A11.2. In 1987, the Cardiff Bay Development Corporation was established to undertake the development of about 1,093ha of land and water in and around Cardiff Bay. A barrage across the mouth of the bay is to be constructed, transforming the mud flats into an inland lake, creating an attractive waterfront which can be utilised for housing, employment and leisure purposes.

A11.3. The Development Corporation, during its existance of 10-12 years, aims to provide 5-6,000 houses, 20,000 jobs and a wide range of leisure facilities in a magnificent setting. The end result envisaged is 'a superlative maritime city which stands comparison with any in the world'.

Ebbw Vale Garden Festival site

A11.4. Ebbw Vale is situated in the heart of the industrial Welsh valleys, 20 miles north of Cardiff. Economic development during the industrial revolution was based on the production of coal from its mines to supply the various local steelworks. With the decline of the coal and steel industries, mines were abandoned, steelworks closed and many areas became derelict.

A11.5. To encourage the revitalisation of the area a successful bid was made for the 1992 Garden Festival to be held in Ebbw Vale on an area of 57ha. The initiative for this came from the local authority, Blaenau Gwent Borough Council and Gwent County Council with the active support of the Welsh Development Agency and the Wales Tourist Board.

A11.6. Land reclamation work started in January 1987 and site development will continue until the opening of the five month festival in May 1992. The site follows the steep sided valley of the River Ebbw and is 2,800m long by 530m wide. It has been designed so that as much of the area as possible can be retained on a permanent basis following the end of the festival. The landscaping includes the planting of 300,000 trees and 450,000 shrubs and includes 1.9ha of water features together with parking facilities for 4,000 cars and 200 coaches. Two-thirds of the site will be retained as a permanent landscaped area and a further 38ha are intended for industrial and commercial use.

A11.7. It is confidently anticipated that conversion of a mainly derelict valley into an attractive landscaped area will provide an ideal setting for development, attracting new industries to the area.

Duport Steelworks, Llanelli

A11.8. Llanelli, situated on the south coast of Wales, was a thriving industrial town depending on the manufacture of steel. The town was separated from its sandy beaches by a string of factories along the coast. With the decline of the steel industry, this area became largely derelict, and the borough council decided to exploit the opportunity of developing the land for tourist and leisure purposes. The land reclamation was funded by the Welsh Development Agency at a cost of almost £2.5M.

A11.9. The site of Duport Steelworks was taken over in 1982 and a scheme undertaken to convert it into a mixture of parkland and residential and commercial areas. On closure of the works, the Duport Company arranged for the dismantling of much of the manufacturing equipment and the council commenced reclamation works in 1986.

A11.10. The focal point was the excavation of a 6ha boating lake. The excavated material was used to form mounds between the lake and the adjacent railway. A highway infrastructure, together with car parks, was completed and the site topsoiled and grass seeded. The northern part of the site was levelled and allocated for housing development. Other parts of the site have been designated for a transit caravan site and a garden centre.

Llanelli wildfowl centre

A11.11. The Llanelli wildfowl centre is sited on an area of land blighted by industrial dereliction. The total cost is approaching £500,000 and the opening of the centre is planned for 1991. It has been created on the north shore of the Burry inlet and adjacent to the tidal marshes which are renowned for the large numbers of breeding and migatory birds which it attracts.

A11.12. The development of the site began in 1985 following extensive consultations with the Wildfowl Trust. A network of ponds was constructed together with a means of controlling the water supply to them. A system of paths was provided together with improved access to the site. A visitor centre has been built as well as observation buildings and a flamingo house.

161

A12. South Western Association

Maintaining river quality during construction of large projects

A12.1. These notes outline the work of consulting engineers in the investigation, planning, monitoring and supervision of major construction schemes to mitigate the effects of water pollution. The schemes are the A30 trunk road, Okehampton bypass (opened in July 1988), the planned 22km improvement of the A30 between Okehampton and Launceston and the Roadford Dam. Each affects a number of major watercourses on the north edge of Dartmoor National Park. The rivers contain salmon and trout and are classified as having a River Quality Objective of either 1A or 1B. Clients are respectively Devon County Council and South West Water. Babtie Shaw and Morton were appointed to assist in monitoring work to determine suitable measures for the prevention of pollution of watercourses on the two road schemes and were also the scheme consultants for the dam.

A30 Okehampton bypass

A12.2. The main constructional problem of the 8km bypass was the formation of a cutting of up to 25m deep across the watershed of the East Okement and West Okement rivers. This cutting was done with the assistance of 22 pumped boreholes to lower the watertable sufficiently to carry out excavations and road construction in the dry. A local environmental group raised the question of the possible pollution of rivers by toxic metals associated with pumped boreholes. Concern was related to old mineworkings for lead and other metals in the area which could cause the release of toxic metals into the watercourses.

Mean concentrations

Parts per million (except for pH)

Parameter	Okehampton BP - (upstream)	River E. Okement (downstream)	Roadford dam - River Wolf Range at 4 points	Mean of lower 3
pH	5.4/7.0	5.8/8.6	5.9/8.6	N/A
Turbidity			6.5 - 11.5	7.1
Colour			26.9 - 35.2	30.6
Suspended solids	1.6	12.3	8.5 - 44.8	9.4
Aluminium	0.11	0.34	0.21 - 1.19	0.23
Manganese	0.017	0.04	0.08 - 0.24	0.09
Iron	0.14	0.428	0.61 - 1.07	0.78
Sulpha e			11.92 - 26.41	15.6
Toxic metals	*	*		
Zinc	*	*		
Copper	*	*		
Cadmium	*	*		
Lead	*	*		
Arsenic	*	*		
Chromium	*	*		
Nickel	*	*		

* Below detectable limits, generally about 0.005 ppm.

A12.3. An initial intensive monitoring investigation was carried out, followed by the taking of 440 chemical samples throughout the two year construction period. Six surveys of the invertebrate population of the rivers upstream and downstream of the construction site were also carried out. These results showed that toxic metals were not present in significant quantities. In the event, the main pollution problem was the discoloration of the rivers below the road crossing points by silt. The peaks of suspended matter coincided with construction but the monitoring of invertebrates showed that this form of contamination had no lasting effect. The analyses of samples from the River East Okement are summarised in the table. These and the many other results obtained suggested that the River Quality Objective of 1A was still met, although when suspended solids exceeded 20ppm, which they did on 20% of occasions, visible pollution was likely.

A12.4. The borehole water did not require treatment to remove toxic metals but silt was a problem. The contractor attempted to control run off from the construction areas but the steep topography did not allow the construction of large lagoons. If more level areas had been available, the construction of lagoons could have prevented some pollution.

Roadford Dam

A12.5. South West Water promoted the Roadford Project to supply water to areas of Devon and Cornwall affected by summer droughts. It entailed construction of a 430m dam and the placement of $1Mm^3$ of carboniferous shales and sandstones in a 40m high embankment. This material was obtained from a local quarry specially opened up in the reservoir basin.

A12.6. Geotechnical investigations showed that the carboniferous rock from the quarry contained pyrites (iron sulphide) and associated minerals such as manganese and aluminium. Pyrites is frequently encountered in coal mining and the resultant effects of red-brown ochre deposits from minewater drainage are widely known. Laboratory experiments showed that, when oxidised in the presence of water, the rocks could produce an acidic solution containing iron and manganese. Measures were taken in the design of the dam to reduce the likelihood of demineralisation in the long term, but a potential water pollution problem was anticipated during construction.

A12.7. As part of the overall monitoring of the whole project, 700 samples were taken for chemical monitoring during construction of the embankment. Water draining from disturbed areas, such as the quarry and the contractor's batching plant, was diverted into a series of lagoons. A summarisation of river water analyses upstream and downstream is given in the table. Occasionally controlled discharges were made from lagoons to the River Wolf. Activities were monitored by a full time Pollution Control Officer who was part of the staff of the Resident Engineer.

A12.8. Monitoring showed that small quantities of rock demineralisation products such as iron, manganese and acidic sulphate are produced when fresh rock is exposed. Also silt from the quarry and other working areas produced noticeable turbidity in drainage waters, especially in winter conditions. Lagoons, if suitably sized, are an effective method of balancing and settling discharges prior to discharge. The criteria used for sizing was 50mm of rainfall in one day over the area disturbed by earthworks. Evaporation and seeping away of lagoon contents occurred in dry weather leaving capacity available for collection of run off in wet weather. In dealing with metals such as iron and manganese, percolation of drainage through woodland was also effective. The analyses demonstrate that there was very little difference in water quality between the upstream end of the cleared reservoir basin and some 1.5km downstream of the embankment, where, on the evidence, the river would meet River Quality Objective 1A.

A12.9. The proposed route of 22km is through the valleys of two rivers which have a high conservation interest and support salmonid fish and otters. There are also marshes and mature woodlands in the valley floors which have an ecological value. Various local groups such as Devon Wildlife Trust have drawn attention to the potential problem of water pollution arising from the roadworks.

A12.10. Regular sampling over a one week period from a pumped borehole at the location of a proposed major cutting and periodic monitoring of the water quality in a chain of static boreholes revealed negligible concentrations of toxic metals such as copper, cadmium, lead and chromium. Levels of aluminium, manganese and iron were sometimes significant and iron levels were very high. The pumped borehole produced significant levels of zinc and aluminium at the start of pumping but they fell away during the week of testing. Comparison of results for total and dissolved metal concentrations showed that settlement or filtration would remove most of them. The proposed treatment methods are settlement of drainage water in lagoons and percolation through woodland or over grassland to reduce turbidity and metal contamination to an acceptable level. The addition of lime or other alkali may be used to counteract acidity and assist in precipitation of metals from solution. Lagoons are sized as for Roadford.

Contractual responsibility and costs

A12.11. Legal responsibility for meeting water quality standards rests with the contractor, who must apply for any discharge consent from NRA. General good practice during construction includes interception ditches at boundaries of the land and control of surface waters around borrow pits, batching plants and areas for disposal of unsuitable material.

A12.12. Some identifiable costs for special provisions for prevention of water pollution on the schemes discussed are:

- Okehampton Bypass (1986-88) constructon cost £16.7M.
    tanks for treatment of toxic metals £20,000;
    consultants fees for monitoring and investigation £37,300;
    chemical analyses £12,100;
    biological monitoring by Freshwater Biological Association £21,000.
- Roadford (1987-89) construction cost £16.1M.
    Consultants fees for monitoring and investigation £24,000;
    erecting, maintaining and removing lagoons £37,500;
- Okehampton-Launceston (1989-90) estimated cost over £40M.
    consultants fees for preliminary investigation,
    chemical analyses, monitoring and feasibility report £16,000.

Conclusion

A12.13. With increased environmental awareness, water quality must be added to the factors considered at an early stage of feasibility studies. Careful investigation and regular monitoring are important in the design of measures to maintain water quality. Compared with the overall costs of the schemes in question, measures for the control of water pollution are relatively small.

Annex B. Membership

Infrastructure Policy Group

Sir Frank Gibb (Chairman)	former Chairman, Taylor Woodrow Group
J. Dromgoole	Director (Council Secretariat), Institution of Civil Engineers
P. J. Andrews	Head of Structural Engineering, Northamptonshire County Council
J. A. Armitt	Joint Managing Director, John Laing Construction
Professor A. Budd	Economic Adviser, Barclays Bank plc
P. A. Cox	former Chairman, Rendel, Palmer and Tritton
Dr J. R. Duffell	Director of Studies, Civil Engineering, Hatfield Polytechnic
E. W. Flaxman	Consultant, Binnie and Partners
Professor G. Fleming	Professor of Civil Engineering, University of Strathclyde
S. F. Hall	Director of Engineering, Rotherham Borough Council
I. W. Hannah	former Director of Civil Engineering, Central Electricity Generating Board
Professor M. A. Laughton	Professor of Electrical & Electronic Engineering Queen Mary and Westfield College
Professor A. D. May	Professor of Transport Engineering, University of Leeds
S. N. Mustow	Consultant, W S Atkins
B. Oldridge	Director of Transportation, Cambridge County Council
Z. Szembek	Consultant, Posford Duvivier
P. J. White	Assistant Director of Civil Engineering, British Railways Board
A. P. Young	Rail Systems Manager, Greater Manchester PTE

POLLUTION

Local Association Teams
(*IPG Support Team Member)

East Anglia	G. G. Ford	T. A. Oakes	R. S. C. Stewart*
East Midlands	B. Raper	J. Trinick	R. S. C. Stewart*
Edinburgh and East of Scotland	R. J. C. Stobie*	D. Gallacher	
Glasgow and West of Scotland	R. J. C. Stobie*	Professor A. Gilchrist	Professor G. Fleming
Home Counties	Dr J. R. Duffell		
Midlands	G. N. Dancer	R. B. Edwards	
Northern Ireland	J. Brennan		
North Western	D. M. Price	J Harrison	
Southern	M. Brocklehurst	O. Simon*	
South Eastern	M. A. Froude	C. Bentley	P. J. Hesketh-Roberts
South Wales	F. L. H. Straw		
South Western	J. E. Bell	P. J. Fells*	A. Street

Chapter Authors

J. Dromgoole P. J. Andrews H. Bernicoff
P. J. Fells Professor G. Fleming R. P. Huxford
B. H. Newman T. H. Nicholson O. Simon
H. Speight F. L. H. Straw R. S. C. Stewart

With thanks for advice from Dr P. H. Kemp, Technical Secretary, Coastal Engineering Research Advisory Committee (CERAC), and Dr M. J. Tooley, Chairman, Environmental Research Centre, University of Durham.

Secretariat

H. Bernicoff S. R. Jones

168